Spotlight on Saints!

Mother Mary

Paul

Gianna Molla

John Bosco

Martin de Porres

Kateri Tekakwitha

Bakhita

Juan Diego

Clare

Andrew Kim Daegeon

Thérèse of Lisieux

Bernardine of Siena

Spotlight on Saints!

A Year of Funny Readers Theater for Today's Catholic Kids

Written by Diana R. Jenkins

Illustrated by Virginia Helen Richards, FSP

Pauline
BOOKS & MEDIA
Boston

Library of Congress Cataloging-in-Publication Data

Jenkins, Diana R.
  Spotlight on saints! : a year of funny readers theater for today's Catholic kids / written by Diana R. Jenkins ; illustrated by Virginia Helen Richards.
    p. cm.
  ISBN 0-8198-7119-2 (pbk.)
  1. Drama in Christian education. 2. Catholic children--Religious life--Juvenile drama. 3. Christian saints--Juvenile drama. I. Richards, Virginia Helen. II. Title.
  BV1534.4.J46 2009
  268'.432--dc22
                                    2008043370

Scripture texts in this work are taken from *The Holy Bible: Contemporary English Version*, © 1995, American Bible Society, 1865 Broadway, New York, NY 10023, and are used by permission. All rights reserved.

Cover design by Mary Joseph Peterson, FSP

Photocopies may be made only of reproducible sections (identified with a copyright notice on the bottom of the first page of each section). The following conditions apply: 1) photocopies must be made by an educator as part of a systematic learning program in a nonprofit educational institution; 2) the photocopies must be provided to students free of charge; 3) the copyright notice must be visible on each copy; 4) commercial use of the photocopies is prohibited. Any other use that is not provided for in this paragraph is subject to written permission from Pauline Books & Media.

"P" and PAULINE are registered trademarks of the Daughters of St. Paul.

Copyright © 2009, Daughters of St. Paul
Text copyright © 2009, Diana R. Jenkins

Published by Pauline Books & Media, 50 Saint Pauls Avenue, Boston, MA 02130-3491

Printed in U.S.A.

www.pauline.org

Pauline Books & Media is the publishing house of the Daughters of St. Paul, an international congregation of women religious serving the Church with the communications media.

1 2 3 4 5 6 7 8 9   13 12 11 10 09

Contents

Introduction

When I was a kid, I loved books about the saints, and I read every single one in our school library—over and over! I was so inspired by these special people who focused their lives on God. Their stories made me want to be a martyr—or at least a better person! To this day, I still find inspiration in the lives of the saints.

Today's kids can learn from the saints, too, and this book helps them do that in a fun way. *Spotlight on Saints! A Year of Funny Readers Theater for Today's Catholic Kids* is a collection of humorous plays about contemporary kids. In each play, a regular kid who is faced with a realistic (but funny) problem learns about a saint and gets inspired to do the right thing. Information about a real saint is spotlighted in each play, but these scripts also emphasize the idea that we are all called to be saints, encouraging children to strive for that goal.

This book is arranged to provide a play for each month of the year. The featured saint in each play has a feast day in the given month. However, many of the plays would be appropriate for other times, too, so you can use them whenever you like. Read on for some suggestions on how to successfully incorporate these plays into your classroom or program.

WHAT IS READERS THEATER ANYWAY?

Readers theater is easier theater! Actors don't memorize their lines—they simply read from their scripts. Because memorization isn't an issue, more students are able to handle large roles. Also, extensive rehearsal isn't necessary. And, unlike "regular" theater, a readers theater production isn't thrown into a tailspin by memory lapses or absences.

Other aspects of readers theater are easy, too. Sets, costumes, props, and even movement are not needed, as the plays are written to work without them. The extras can be included if desired, but readers theater works even if the actors just sit there and read.

How Do I Get Started?

Before you use a readers theater play, read it yourself and make sure that the content, theme, and vocabulary are appropriate for your students. Decide whether you need to preview any concepts or vocabulary. If you are thinking about staging the play for an audience, consider which students might fit which roles, but don't set your cast just yet.

Once you decide on a play, make as many copies of the script as there are parts, plus one for yourself. Highlight one character's lines in each copy (except yours) to make it easier for kids to read. Covering or binding the scripts will help them last through multiple readings.

After giving students time to read through their scripts silently, have them read the play aloud from their desks. You can change roles with each scene to involve more students. (This also allows you to see how different kids handle different roles. If you decide later to stage the play, you can choose your cast according to who fits which character instead of who can memorize the most lines.) This kind of read-through makes a good one-time supplemental activity in your classroom, but you can do much more with readers theater. For example, you could have students read a particular script multiple times on different days. The repetition gives you several opportunities to teach comprehension skills like character traits, motivation, story structure, theme, and cause and effect. And rereading allows children to relax about the reading itself and develop a deeper understanding of the characters and the theme of the play.

Multiple readings also improve fluency and expression. You can help with these skills by sharing the presentation suggestions included in each play's introductory material and by asking questions about the characters' feelings and motivation. If a student has difficulty with expression, "echo reading" can help. You model the lines with good expression and have the student copy you. It doesn't usually take much of this practice to get a young actor on the right track. Allowing students to record themselves as they read their lines and listen afterward also develops better expression.

After several readings, you might want to move students from their desks to a traditional readers theater setup at the front of the room. The actors in readers theater usually sit on stools or chairs throughout the play, holding and reading their scripts. Sometimes the actors sit with their backs to the audience, "entering" by facing front and reading their lines and "exiting" by turning around again. The narrator might stand to one side or read from a lectern. Getting away from their desks can make readers theater more fun for your students and motivate them to further improve their performances.

What About Performing For an Audience?

You may decide to use readers theater only as a supplemental activity in your classroom. However, you could be tempted—or persuaded!—to stage a performance for a real, live audience. How do you make the transition?

First, rehearse enough that actors can read with good expression and look up from their scripts occasionally. (But don't over-rehearse! This is easier theater, re-member?) Be sure to go through the whole play at least once without stopping. Set up your first performance with an audience that's not too threatening; a group of younger children works well. Later, you can try performing for scarier audiences such as peers or adults.

After some successful performances, your kids may naturally move toward something more like "regular" theater. They might make more facial expressions, gesture, or ask to act things out. At this point, you could abandon the traditional setup and allow students to enter and exit and to move around the stage, holding their scripts. The plays in this book include some directions for movement in case you decide to do this.

Eventually, you may discover that your kids are memorizing some lines on their own. They might even ask to drop the scripts and do a "real" play. Or maybe you'll decide to encourage that yourself and move completely into "regular" theater. That's a great experience for your class, but remember that you don't have to put together a big production. Feel free to stick to the simple, traditional readers theater format.

The closer you get to a regular theater performance, the more likely it is that your students will ask for sets, props, and costumes. This book includes sugges-tions about these extras in case you want to include them, but the scripts are written to make them unnecessary. If you decide to use these items, hold off on rehears-ing with them right away as they distract kids from developing their characters and improving their performances.

To involve more students, you can link several plays together into a longer pro-gram. While you work with one group, other casts could be reading through their scripts together or making invitations, programs, sets, props, or costumes. While an absence isn't a catastrophe in readers theater, it doesn't hurt to have one cast watch another cast's rehearsal or read another group's play just in case.

Is It Really Worth It?

Every child can benefit from theater experiences. Of course, plays about a partic-ular subject matter (such as the saints) motivate kids to learn important information, but theater develops other academic skills, too. Performing a play—even just from their desks—helps students develop language arts skills such as listening, reading, and speaking. You can also use theater to improve writing skills by asking students to rewrite their lines, add new lines, or write the endings to interrupted lines. (The last one is really a must! Nothing is more awkward than an actor pausing before the character is actually interrupted by another. If the rest of the line is written out, the reader can keep going until the next person breaks in or until the end of the line if necessary.) Kids can also write alternate endings to plays or make up their own scripts.

Theater yields nonacademic benefits, too. The hope is that reading the plays in this book will inspire kids to follow in the footsteps of the saints and make positive changes in their own lives. Staging a play from this book—or any other script—builds character in other ways, too. Putting on a performance takes skills like working hard, setting goals, meeting challenges, staying patient, and cooperating with others. (And that's not just for the teacher!) Children experience a real sense of accomplishment from their individual successes as well as the group's achievements. And the self-esteem they develop in theater carries over into the rest of their lives!

Connor Says

SUMMARY

Connor believes he has what it takes to be a great leader. But when he's put in charge of the youth group fundraiser, he finds that nobody appreciates his vision or respects his orders. The great leaders of history never had this much trouble!

COSTUMES/SETS/PROPS

All characters can wear contemporary clothing. Connor might get some humor out of wearing a jacket and posing with his hand inside like Napoleon. The little kid in Scene Four could wear oversized clothes and carry a big stuffed toy.

A few chairs can be used during the youth group meetings. A table to one side can serve as the bake sale table.

Connor needs a book about Saint John Bosco for Scene Nine, or his script could be covered to suggest such a book. He could use a clipboard and pen during the scenes at church, perhaps clipping his script onto the clipboard. Other props can be mimed, but, if desired, containers of baked goods and a cash box could be used.

PRESENTATION

Connor becomes more and more domineering and impatient as the play goes on.

James tries to be understanding, but eventually he can't take Connor's attitude any more.

Mrs. Esposito should show that she's sometimes having trouble keeping her patience.

The extra youth group kids should react to what happens even when they have no lines.

CAST

Narrator

Connor

Mrs. Esposito, the youth group sponsor

Youth group: Andy, Francesca, James, Brittany, extra kids (as desired)

Little kid

ABOUT SAINT JOHN BOSCO

John Bosco was born in Italy in 1815. As a child, he had a great desire to learn, but his family's poverty often kept him from his studies. When he finally became a priest, he saw firsthand the poor treatment that needy children received. He gathered these children to him with fun activities and then led them gently to God. Using kindness instead of the usual harsh discipline of his day, he encouraged piety and good character in his charges. Despite many difficulties, he established homes, schools, and job-training programs to help needy children live better lives. John Bosco died in 1888, but his influence continues today in the work of the Salesians, the religious order he formed to serve the young and poor with charitable works. Saint John Bosco's feast day is January 31. He is the patron saint of youth and of editors.

Connor Says

Scene One

Narrator: Connor had never been in charge of anything. Teachers never chose him to lead group projects. Camp counselors never put him out front on hikes. He never got elected to anything. Still, he felt sure he had that special something.

Connor: *(entering)* It's called leadership potential. I read about it. Alexander the Great had leadership potential. So did Genghis Khan. And Napoleon. Oh, and that Simon guy.

Narrator: Simon?

Connor: You know. The Simon who's always saying "Simon says." Now there's a guy with leadership potential! If I just had the chance, I could be a great leader, too.

Narrator: Uh-huh. *(to audience as Mrs. Esposito and youth group enter)* Finally, Connor got his big leadership opportunity when something exciting happened at his youth group.

Mrs. Esposito: It's time to vote! Who wants to do the mission trip this summer?

Youth Group: *(waving hands)* Yes! Let's do it! You bet! *Etc.*

Mrs. Esposito: Wonderful! Now we just have to come up with the money to pay our expenses.

Andy: Our parents will help us out with that.

Mrs. Esposito: I'm sure they will, Andy, but we need to raise most of the funds ourselves. For example, we might be able to perform some kind of service for money.

Andy: Our parents will pay us to do stuff. My parents will even pay me *not* to do stuff.

Francesca: *(muttering)* Hey, I'll pay you to stop talking.

Andy: Yeah! Stuff like that!

James: Shouldn't we have somebody in charge of our fundraising, Mrs. Esposito?

Mrs. Esposito: Good idea! We need someone responsible running things.

Narrator: *(to Connor)* Psst! This is the exciting part! You could be that person.

Connor: Oh, yeah. *(waving hand frantically)* I can do it! Pick me! Pick me!

Mrs. Esposito: Have you ever been in charge of something like this, Connor?

Connor: No, but I can do it. Pleeeeeeease?

Mrs. Esposito: Well … all right.

Francesca: But are you sure you can handle it, Connor?

Connor: Of course! Believe me—you guys will be glad to have me in charge of things.

Narrator: But they weren't. Not. At. All.

Scene Two

Narrator: *(as all exit except Connor and James)* Connor's first task as a leader was to think of fundraising projects. He shared his ideas with his friend James just before the next meeting.

Connor: I am really an idea man. Guess how many fundraising ideas I have.

James: Um … seven?

Connor: Dude. I told you: I'm an idea man. I came up with forty-seven ideas!

James: Forty-seven! Wow!

Connor: I have the usual stuff like bake sales, but I have some different ideas, too. Like Hire-a-Laugh. That's where people pay us to pretend we like their jokes. And Vegetable-of-the-Day.

James: People pay us to pretend we're vegetables?

Connor: Sheesh! It's a good thing I'm the one in charge. Remember in kindergarten when we got to wear that hat shaped like a cake on our birthdays? We'll dye a chef's hat green like a big chunk of broccoli, and people will pay to wear it all day and look hilarious.

James: Wow. You have some ideas, all right.

Connor: Yeah. Everybody's going to flip when they hear them all.

James: *All* of them? But the group can't decide on that many choices.

Connor: Oh, yeah. What am I thinking? I'm the leader! Deciding is my job, right?

James: Well, that's part of—

Connor: I'll have to think … OK! I've decided! Sorry, James, but you'll have to wait until the meeting starts to find out which one of my ideas we'll be using.

James: Which *one?* Just one?

Connor: I hear you, but we can't do them all. Boy. Leaders sure have to make some tough calls.

James: Yeah, but sometimes leaders have to consider other people's opinions, Connor.

Connor: I agree! Hey, everybody's free to tell me how much they like my ideas. I'm not a dictator.

James: Gee. That's great to know.

Scene Three

Narrator: *(as Mrs. Esposito and youth group enter)* When the meeting started, Connor finally got to display his leadership potential.

Connor: OK, you guys! I have a great idea that'll make us tons of money for our trip. I mean … we'll be able to ride in limousines and eat steaks!

Youth Group: Cool! Wow! Great! *Etc.*

Mrs. Esposito: I'm sure Connor is speaking figuratively. This *is* a mission trip, after all.

Connor: Oh, yeah. Right. I was just giving a little pep talk. That's the kind of leader I am.

Francesca: So what's your big idea?

Connor: Pet-a-Rattlesnake!

Mrs. Esposito: P-p-pardon me?

Connor: See, we decorate this box with pictures of rattlesnakes and cut a hole in the side and charge people to reach in and pet the rattlesnake.

Andy: I don't think my parents will allow me to do that. They like for me to avoid danger.

Connor: Dude! We'll just put a fake snake and a baby rattle inside the box.

Francesca: Why not use one of my grandma's old boots and tell people it's a crocodile?

Connor: Like anybody will fall for that.

Mrs. Esposito: I'm sorry, Connor, but we can't use deception to raise money. That's wrong.

Youth Group, except James: Really! No kidding! Brother! *Etc.*

James: Tell them one of your other ideas, Connor.

Connor: OK! Why not? I have tons of them.

Narrator: Connor presented idea after idea to the youth group, but nobody liked any of them.

Mrs. Esposito: *(tired)* You're really clever, Connor, but maybe this isn't the job for you.

Connor: *(desperately)* Bake sales! We can have bake sales!

Brittany: Finally—a decent idea.

Andy: Yeah. Bake sales make a lot of money. Our parents—

Mrs. Esposito: Who wants bake sales? *(kids start raising hands)* Good! See you all next time!

Connor: *(as others except Francesca and James exit)* I have all these fantastic ideas, but people want to do stupid old ordinary bake sales?

Francesca: Your other ideas were ridiculous! *(exiting)* Like anybody wants an engraved pickle!

Connor: You know, James, being a leader is harder than I thought. But I'm going to make this bake sale idea work. Nobody appreciated my vision, but they will respect how I run things.

James: I'm sure they will.

Connor: They'd better.

Scene Four

Narrator: On Sunday, Connor waited in the church vestibule with a clipboard and a master plan.

Connor: A good leader always has a master plan. And an official-looking clip-board.

Narrator: I doubt Alexander the Great had a clipboard. Or Genghis Khan, either.

Connor: Well, I'm sure Simon carries one all the time.

Narrator: Right. *(to audience)* Connor caught the youth group kids as they came in.

Connor: *(as Brittany enters)* Listen up, Brittany! Bake sale. Next Sunday. After church. Bring chocolate cupcakes. Home-baked goods only!

Brittany: But I don't know how to cook.

Connor: You can learn how. It's not that hard. See you next Sunday.

Brittany: Gee ... aren't you ... I don't know ...

Connor: I believe the word you're looking for is "organized."

Brittany: Right. Thanks. I was thinking the word was "bossy." How silly of me! *(exits)*

Francesca: *(entering with Andy)* What's with the clipboard?

Connor: Listen up! Bake sale. Next Sunday. After church. Andy, make fruit tarts. Francesca, make brownies: some with nuts, some without, some with icing, some—

Francesca: Who made you the boss of the world?

Connor: That would be Mrs. Esposito.

Andy: *(to Francesca)* He's right about that.

Francesca: Mrs. Esposito put him in charge of our fundraising—that's all.

Connor: And we're talking about fundraising. So you have to do what I say.

Francesca: I guess. But that doesn't make you a big shot.

Connor: Look, this isn't about me. This is about the people who need our help. Don't you care about sharing the word of God with them and making a difference in their lives?

Francesca: Of course, I do!

Connor: Then make the brownies, Francesca. Make. The. Brownies.

Francesca: OK, OK! I'll make the stupid brownies.

Andy: And I'll make those tarts. Lots of them. *(moved)* You've really inspired me, man.

Narrator: *(as Francesca and Andy exit)* So Connor gave all the kids their orders. His friend James came in last.

James: *(entering)* Hi, Connor.

Connor: Listen up! Bake sale. Next Sunday. After church. Bring—

James: Why are you talking like that?

Connor: I'm displaying a commanding presence.

James: Yeah, you're commanding, all right.

Connor: Thanks! So bring some banana nut bread next week.

James: *(muttering as he exits)* Yes, Your Majesty.

Connor: OK. That's everybody. Now we're all set.

Little kid: *(enters)* Excuse me, Mister. Where's the bathroom?

Connor: Down the hall and to the right.

Little kid: Thanks, Mister. *(exit)*

Connor: Mister! Ha! I really am a natural-born leader.

Scene Five

Narrator: When next Sunday rolled around, Connor got his clipboard and waited.

Brittany: *(entering)* Here are the chocolate cupcakes.

Connor: They're not homemade!

Brittany: I told you, I don't know how to cook.

Connor: You had a whole week to learn! Are you just too stupid to get it?

Brittany: *(upset)* Sorry! *(exits as Francesca and Andy enter)*

Andy: Here's my pie. My parents helped me make it. See how we crimped the crust?

Connor: Pie! You were supposed to bring tarts. Lots of tarts. You said I inspired you.

Andy: Oh, yeah. I guess I forgot about that. Well, a pie is just a big tart.

Connor: And you're a big dope! What's with those brownies, Francesca? Couldn't you have smoothed the icing out a little bit?

Francesca: I was trying to put it on nice and thick.

Connor: Well, it looks like mud!

Francesca: Well, it tastes just fine!

Connor: Well, come back after Mass, and see if you can sell any of your old mud brownies!

Francesca: Gee. Is that one of your pep talks? *(exiting with Andy)*

Narrator: Despite all his leadershipness … leaderability … leaderation? … things just didn't work out according to Connor's master plan. Some people brought the wrong things. Some people brought nothing. Some people didn't even show up!

Connor: Sheesh! How hard is it to follow orders?

James: *(entering)* Hi, Connor. Here's the banana bread.

Connor: Don't you mean banana *nut* bread?

James: I left out the nuts because some people are allergic.

Connor: Aaugh! I'm surrounded by idiots!

James: Hey!

Connor: Sorry, James. I'm just upset. Nobody's doing anything right. I'll bet Alexander the Great didn't have this kind of trouble. When he told people to do something, they did it.

James: Of course! They didn't want anything bad to happen … like their village getting destroyed. They were afraid of the guy! You don't want to be that kind of leader, do you? *(exits)*

Connor: Hmmm …

Narrator: Well? Do you?

Connor: I'm thinking! I'm thinking!

Narrator: Are you serious?

Connor: Of course not. Just joking. Heh. Heh.

Scene Six

Narrator: To Connor's surprise, the youth group made quite a bit of money on the bake sale.

Mrs. Esposito: (entering) If all the bake sales go this well, we'll soon have the funds we need.

Connor: Don't worry. I have everything under control—and I can guarantee our future success.

Mrs. Esposito: My. Well. All right then. (exits as James enters)

James: So did we make a lot of money?

Connor: We did pretty well—thanks to me!

James: But you didn't bring in anything to sell.

Connor: I have more important things to do than bake cookies, James.

James: Yeah. You're the big boss.

Connor: And it's a good thing. Even *with* my guidance, lots of people slacked off. I'll bet Genghis Khan didn't let anybody get away with stuff like that. I need to whip our group into shape.

James: But you could be a different kind of leader. Like John Bosco. Remember him?

Connor: Not really.

James: We read about him in school. He was a priest in Italy back in the 1800s, and he helped the poor boys who lived in the streets. He taught them about Jesus and gave them a home and—

Connor: Wait a minute! I do remember him. He was a saint.

James: That's right!

Connor: I hate to disappoint you, but I'm no saint.

James: (muttering) No kidding! (louder) I mean … you don't have to be a saint. But you could learn from Saint John Bosco. He was a great leader for those kids, but he did things in a different way from Alexander the Great and those other people you keep talking about.

Connor: Look, I'm not going to … to chop off any heads … or wreck a village … or anything. I just want to get everybody to give their best. What's wrong with that?

James: Nothing, but you don't have to be so hard on people. And bossy. And … and mean.

Connor: Hey, sometimes the person in charge has to be tough, OK?

James: *(sighs)* Connor, the best leaders are the ones people *want* to follow.

Connor: Yeah, yeah. Like Saint John Bosco. I told you: I'm no saint. Just drop it, will you?

James: *(exiting)* I was only trying to help!

Connor: Like I need *his* help. I have leadership potential—and I'm not afraid to use it!

Scene Seven

Narrator: *(as Mrs. Esposito and youth group enter)* At the next meeting, Mrs. Esposito praised everybody for the successful bake sale.

Mrs. Esposito: And how about a round of applause for our leader? Good job, Connor. *(claps)*

Youth Group: *(clap only a few times)*

Mrs. Esposito: Connor, is there anything you need to say about our next bake sale?

Connor: Yes, ma'am. *(to kids)* The first bake sale wasn't bad—but it wasn't as successful as it could have been. And I think we all know why.

Francesca: Poor leadership?

Connor: Funny. Look, I had everything well-organized, but some of you disappointed me. And, even worse, you disappointed the people we're planning to help. If you care about those people, you won't let that happen again. You do care, don't you?

Youth Group: *(mutters)*

Mrs. Esposito: I know everybody here cares very deeply. Isn't that true?

Youth Group: *(mutters a little louder)*

Connor: OK then. How about if you all make the same thing this Sunday that you were supposed to make for the last sale? You know … the stuff I *told* you to make.

Brittany: Just because you say we have to do something doesn't mean we actually have to do it.

Francesca: *(muttering)* Yeah. Who cares what Connor says?

James: Why can't we bring whatever we want?

Connor: We could end up with too much of one thing. That wouldn't be good, would it?

Youth Group: *(mutters)*

Connor: *Would* it?

Youth Group: *(mutters a little louder)*

Connor: OK then. Let's stick to my plan. And listen ... everybody needs to come to our table after Mass and help sell stuff. I'll expect to see you there. Each and every one of you. Or else.

Mrs. Esposito: Or else?

Connor: I mean ... or else ... I won't see you until the next meeting.

Mrs. Esposito: Oh. Well, let's move on to our Scripture reading.

Connor: *(to James as others exit)* There! Now that's leadership.

James: If you say so.

Connor: I do say so. And what I say goes. Hey! I'm just like that Simon guy.

James: I don't know who he is, and I don't care. All I know is: you're not Connor any more. And I don't want to be friends with the person you've become. *(exits)*

Connor: *(calling after him)* Whatever! *(to self)* Now I know why they say it's lonely at the top.

Scene Eight

Narrator: Connor told himself that losing James's friendship was a sacrifice he had to make to accomplish his goals. But the next Sunday, he started wondering if being in charge was worth the sacrifices. He arrived at church early and waited for everybody else. And waited ... and waited ...

Connor: Where are they? Sheesh! Do I have to ... Oh! There's somebody. *(as Brittany enters)* Where have you been? It's almost time for church to start.

Brittany: Already? Gee. I'd better go on in.

Connor: Hey, where's your stuff for the bake sale?

Brittany: Was that today?

Connor: How could you forget?

Brittany: I guess I'm just stupid.

Connor: Oh, I get it. Well, listen, you're going to be sorry when I tell Mrs. Esposito on you.

Brittany: Go ahead. Be sure to mention how you insulted me. *(exits)*

Connor: Unbelievable! Well, I don't need a loser like that on my team. There's Andy!

Andy: *(entering)* Here are my tarts.

Connor: These aren't homemade!

Andy: Hey, you're not the boss of me! Or my parents! And you're not getting another crumb out of us! *(timidly)* OK? *(exits)*

Connor: What's his problem?

Francesca: *(entering)* I brought some cupcakes.

Connor: You were supposed to bring brownies. Some with nuts, some without, some—

Francesca: That table looks pretty empty, but if you don't want my cupcakes ...

Connor: I'll take them!

Francesca: The icing is kind of lumpy. Good luck selling them.

Connor: Aren't you coming back after Mass to help?

Francesca: Nope. And I don't think anybody else is either.

Connor: What? I can't do everything by myself!

Francesca: You can do it. Don't give up. How's that for a pep talk? *(exits)*

Connor: This is like a plot! They're getting back at me just because I tried to do my job.

Narrator: Other youth group kids seemed to be in on the plot, too. Most claimed to have forgotten the bake sale. Only a few brought baked goods—the wrong things, of course.

Connor: This is a disaster! What am I going to do?

Narrator: *(as James enters)* Finally, James came in with a huge box full of treats.

Connor: Thanks! You saved my life, man!

James: Hey, not everything is about you and your plan for world domination. I just felt the mission trip was more important than your power trip. *(sighs)* I'll come back later to help. *(exits)*

Connor: Man! What kind of guy lays it on the line like that?

Narrator: The kind of guy who makes a good friend because he really cares about what matters and isn't afraid to be honest?

Connor: *(sadly)* Yeah.

Scene Nine

Narrator: Connor went into Mass then, but he had a hard time paying attention. He was too busy thinking about how he'd messed up his big leadership opportunity.

Connor: I *have* been on some kind of power trip. Who wants to follow a dictator like me?

Narrator: Um … nobody?

Connor: Right. Nobody cares what Connor says. I get that now.

Narrator: James helped at the bake sale table without speaking to Connor. After everything was sold, James left and Connor counted up the money.

Mrs. Esposito: *(entering)* So how did we do?

Connor: We didn't make as much as before. I'm sorry, Mrs. Esposito. I … I've been having some problems with this leadership thing. I think you'd better put someone else in charge.

Mrs. Esposito: I'm not ready to give up on you, Connor. You really do have some leadership potential. You're organized. You set goals. Sometimes, you're even inspirational.

Connor: Really?

Mrs. Esposito: Yes, really. So think about what kind of leader you want to be, OK? *(exits)*

Connor: If only I could be like that saint James was talking about. Now there was a guy with leadership potential. I wonder how he did it? Hey! Maybe I could … *(exits)*

Narrator: Connor had never taken much interest in the saints before, but he studied up on Saint John Bosco.

Connor: *(enters reading book)* Cool! Saint John knew how to do stunts like juggling. He sounds a lot more fun than Napoleon! *(turns page)* And he was so nice to the needy kids. When they did something wrong, he encouraged them with kind words instead of coming down too hard. Maybe Alexander the Great should have tried that. *(turns page)* Wow! Saint John really helped those kids do something with their lives. But he guided them gently instead of bossing them. *(sighs)* That's the kind of leader I'd like to be. But everybody's probably too fed up to give me another chance. What's the point of even trying to change?

Narrator: *(turns a page in Connor's book and points)*

Connor: *(reads then looks up)* He kept trying to do God's will. He never gave up. I … I have to give it another shot.

Scene Ten

Narrator: *(as Mrs. Esposito and youth group enter)* Nobody looked happy when Connor got up to speak at the next meeting, but he thought of Saint John Bosco and plowed ahead.

Connor: I asked Mrs. Esposito to let me talk to you guys. I'm really sorry for how I've been acting. This group deserves a good leader. But I got out of control and became … well …

Francesca: Bossy?

Brittany: Domineering?

Andy: Mean?

James: A harsh, unforgiving, tin-plated dictator with a heart of stone?

Mrs. Esposito: Give him a chance!

Connor: It's OK. Everything they said is true. I'm really sorry. I hope you can all forgive me. And if you give me another chance, I'll do better. I'm sure I'll make more mistakes. Hey, I'm no saint. But I'll try to be a good leader instead of a tin-plated dictator with a heart of stone.

James: That's *harsh, unforgiving,* tin-plated dictator with a heart of stone.

Connor: Yeah. That. Anyway … thanks for listening. *(sits)*

Mrs. Esposito: So … what does everybody think?

Andy: He really *is* organized. And he has some good ideas.

Francesca: *I-de-a.* One idea. And he blew that one.

Brittany: But you have to admit he's creative. And he did apologize.

James: And promise to change.

Francesca: Well … I guess we can give him another chance.

Mrs. Esposito: Does everyone agree?

Youth Group: Sure! Why not? OK! *Etc.*

Connor: Thanks, you guys! I won't let you down.

Narrator: So Connor changed completely, and soon he was beloved by all who … *(Everyone gives him a look.)* Well, OK. He still gets pretty bossy sometimes. But he tries to remember what he learned about Saint John Bosco. And he's getting better about leading with kindness.

Connor: *(to individuals as they exit)* Great job! Nice try! Looking good! You rock! *Etc.*

Narrator: *(as Connor exits)* Yeah. That's the kind of stuff Connor says now.

SAINT JOHN BOSCO

Selena's Best Shot

SUMMARY

When Selena misses the crucial shot in a basketball game, nobody will forgive her. She decides to get back at her critics by not forgiving anybody for anything! Her harsh attitude hurts her friends, but she doesn't care—until she learns about true forgiveness from Saint Bakhita.

COSTUMES/SETS/PROPS

All actors can wear contemporary clothing. The team could wear basketball attire.

A few desks or tables with chairs could serve as the various classrooms in the play.

All props can be mimed, but if props are desired, the following could be used: textbooks and other school supplies, lunch trays with food, art supplies, and a phone.

PRESENTATION

At the beginning of the play, sounds of the basketball game could be heard off-stage.

Selena can't quite hide that she is hurt by everyone's comments and by their later reactions to her unforgiving attitude. Because she's hurt, she's overly sensitive.

In Scene Eight, Selena pretends to dial the phone before speaking to each of her friends.

In classes, kids can mime working, painting, etc.

CAST

Narrator

Selena

Selena's teammates: Jake, Tasha, Mitch, Caitlyn

Selena's other friends: Frannie, Pablo

Mr. Pulaski, social studies teacher

Ms. Teller, math teacher

Mrs. Ortez, art teacher

ABOUT SAINT BAKHITA

Bakhita was born around 1869 in the Darfur region of Africa. She was so young when she was kidnapped by slave traders that she forgot her real name and went by the one they gave her—"Bakhita" or "lucky one." She was sold to several unkind owners and suffered harsh treatment and even mutilation. When still in her teens, she was acquired by a family who took her to Italy to care for their young daughter. The two girls attended a boarding school run by the Canossian sisters, and there Bakhita became a Christian. Because slavery was illegal in Italy, she was able to refuse to leave the school when the family returned to Africa. Eventually, Bakhita became a Canossian sister, forgiving all who had wronged her and devoting her life to treating others with the kindness she had been denied for so long. Saint Bakhita's feast day is February 8. She is the patron of workers.

Selena's Best Shot

Scene One

Narrator: *(excited)* It was the most exciting game of the season. No! It was the most exciting *moment* of the season. All Selena had to do was make just one more basket, and her team would move on to the tournament. She aimed! She shot! *(dreary tone)* She missed.

Jake: *(as team enters)* Way to go, Selena.

Tasha: You should have taken more time to aim.

Caitlyn: And put more power behind your shot.

Mitch: You cracked under the pressure, didn't you?

Selena: No! I don't know! Look, I did my best.

Jake: Well, it wasn't good enough.

Caitlyn: *(scolding)* Jake!

Jake: Not that we're criticizing you or anything.

Caitlyn: Don't feel bad, Selena. We're just disappointed. We shouldn't be taking it out on you.

Selena: Oh, it's OK, Caitlyn. I know I messed up. And I'm sorry, OK?

Tasha: Sure.

Mitch: OK.

Jake: We understand. *(exiting with Tasha, Mitch)* Not that I'm criticizing, you know, but that shot wasn't even close.

Caitlyn: Don't worry. They'll get over it.

Selena: Oh, I'm not worried. They don't bother me. Not one bit.

Caitlyn: Good! *(exits)*

Selena: *(very upset)* How can they say that stuff about me? They're not perfect. So where do they ... *(acting cool)* I mean ... they don't bother me. *(snorts)* Like I care what they think.

Narrator: So Selena—

Selena: Why should I care?

Narrator: So Selena—

Selena: What if they criticize me? I mean ... I don't care.

Narrator: *(quickly)* So Selena didn't care about what the other kids said.

Selena: *(snorts)* Not at all. *(exits)*

Scene Two

Narrator: *(as Frannie, Pablo, and team enter)* Of course, everyone in school was disappointed about ending the season as losers. So they couldn't stop talking about Selena's last shot.

Frannie: I could have made that shot from the bleachers. And I'm not even on the team.

Pablo: My grandmother could have made that shot from the concession stand.

Jake: Hey, I could make that shot right now.

Caitlyn: Huh?

Jake: I mean ... if I could shoot backwards ... like ... through time ... There's Selena!

Selena: *(entering)* Hi!

Jake: Not that I'm criticizing, but did you make that shot with your eyes closed?

Selena: Why are you *still* talking about that?

Mitch: Because ... we're *still* losers.

Selena: I tried to make the shot. I really tried.

Frannie: Well, I could have made that shot from the bleachers.

Pablo: My grandmother could have made that shot from the concession stand.

Jake: Hey, I could make … um … We could be champions!

Others: Yeah. You're right. That's true. *Etc.*

Selena: You don't know that! We still had to make it through the tournament.

Others: Yeah. You're right. That's true. *Etc.*

Jake: Whatever.

Others: Yeah. You're right. That's true. *Etc.*

Selena: You guys are never going to forgive me for making that one little mistake, are you?

Others: *(after a pause)* Yeah. You're right. That's true. *Etc.*

Selena: I knew it! *(exits)*

Caitlyn: You guys!

Jake: We're just joking.

Frannie: Kind of.

Caitlyn: You hurt her feelings, you know.

Mitch: Oh, she's all right.

Jake: Yeah. I don't think a little teasing is going to crush her.

Caitlyn: I guess.

Narrator: *(as everyone exits)* But Selena was fed up with everybody's comments. And she was ready to fight back.

Selena: *(entering)* You bet! And if people can't forgive me, then I'm not going to forgive them.

Narrator: For what?

Selena: For … for anything!

Scene Three

Narrator: *(as Mr. Pulaski and kids enter)* The next day in social studies, Mr. Pulaski put everybody into groups for a project on the American presidents.

Mr. Pulaski: *(pointing to kids)* OK, Group Five, your president is William Henry Harrison.

Jake: But he was president for less than a month. We can't write much about him.

Mr. Pulaski: I see your point. You know, I'd love to see a report about my favorite president.

Jake: We'll do him. *(to group)* Right?

Others, except Selena: Sure. OK. Yeah. *Etc.*

Mr. Pulaski: OK then—Franklin Delano Roosevelt it is! Let's get busy, everybody. *(exits)*

Selena: Way to go, Jake. Roosevelt was elected president four times. He was president longer than anybody.

Tasha: Oh, no!

Pablo: Our report will have to be huge.

Selena: Right. We'll be writing way more than the other groups. Gee, thanks, Jake.

Jake: Sorry, everybody. I didn't think about that.

Selena: Well, you should have. You didn't use your head, and now we all have to do more work. And it's all your fault. I mean ... *(mocking)* not that I'm criticizing you or anything.

Jake: Wait. Are you trying to get back at me?

Selena: Why would I be doing that?

Jake: Right. Because I haven't done anything to you.

Selena: Of course not. Like I care about anything you do anyway.

Caitlyn: Hey, let's make some plans. I'll bet the job won't seem so big once we get organized.

Selena: A mountain of work is still a mountain of work no matter how you stack it up. Thanks a million, Jake.

Jake: Brother.

Scene Four

Narrator: The group got everything planned by the end of class, even though Selena kept interrupting to point out how Jake's mistake was costing them all. No forgiveness there!

Selena: Nope.

Narrator: *(as Ms. Teller enters)* Next, Selena had math class.

Ms. Teller: OK, let's check last night's homework. Please swap papers with your neighbor.

Narrator: Selena and Tasha checked each other's answers as the teacher read through them.

Ms. Teller: *(super fast)* One yard, twenty-seven, 356, no, 2,385.27, Albuquerque, one and a half, four million, 3:56 pm, even, Susan, square root of sixty-four, eighteen, 50,305, indubitably, the power of ten, odd, the first train, 290,000, fifty-seven years, thirteen, impossible, three dimes and two quarters, yes, my aunt's petunias. There! Now take off four points for each incorrect answer.

Narrator: And when Selena got her paper back—

Selena: WHAT! An F?

Narrator: When Selena got her—

Selena: This can't be right! It can't!

Narrator: *(quickly)* When Selena got her paper back, she flipped out.

Ms. Teller: Calm down. Let me see your paper. Hmmm … Oh, I see. Tasha got off by one. Really, you have 100 percent. OK, class. Pass in your papers and open your books to page 175.

Tasha: Sorry about that, Selena.

Selena: Like your being sorry is going to help me when I'm flunking out of school.

Tasha: But everything turned out OK. You're not flunking.

Selena: No thanks to you! I can't believe you did that to me.

Tasha: Why are you getting so upset? I just made one little mistake.

Selena: You could have ruined my grade!

Jake: Gee, Selena, give it a rest.

Ms. Teller: Stop talking over there!

Selena: See what you did, Jake? You got us all in trouble. Between that and the Franklin Roosevelt fiasco, don't you think you've done enough damage for one day?

Jake: Sheesh! Are you ever going to forgive me for that?

Selena: I'm thinking ... no.

Ms. Teller: QUIET!

Selena: *(to Jake, after a pause)* That was your fault.

Scene Five

Narrator: *(as others except Selena, Mitch, and Caitlyn exit)* At lunch, Mitch got the last slice of pizza.

Selena: How could you do that? You know I love pizza. But, no, you had to hog the last one and leave me with the tuna casserole. I hate tuna.

Caitlyn: That's chicken casserole.

Selena: So not the point, Caitlyn.

Mitch: I got in line before you!

Selena: You mean you shoved into line before me. That was totally wrong.

Mitch: Give me a break!

Selena: No way!

Caitlyn: *(to Mitch)* I was right. We really did hurt her feelings.

Mitch: *(to Caitlyn)* Look, it's not our fault if she can't take a little joking around.

Narrator: *(as Mitch and Caitlyn exit and Frannie and Pablo enter)* In Drama, Selena, Frannie, and Pablo performed their *Tom Sawyer* skit. Of course, things didn't go perfectly ...

Selena: Pablo, you dope! You called me "Aunt Molly" instead of "Aunt Polly." Hello? I'm like a major character in literature. You don't go changing my name.

Pablo: Sorry!

Selena: You sure are. You, too, Frannie. Becky Thatcher shouldn't giggle every three seconds.

Frannie: I was nervous, OK?

Selena: So you cracked under pressure. How is that my problem?

Pablo: *(to Frannie)* What's the matter with her?

Frannie: *(to Pablo)* Do you think she's upset over what we said?

Pablo: *(to Frannie)* We didn't say anything that wasn't true.

Narrator: *(as Frannie and Pablo exit)* All day long, Selena pounced on every mistake, every imperfection, every misspoken word, every *thing!* Whenever she could have forgiven someone, she didn't. She didn't even forgive people when she got mad at them for doing something they really didn't need to be forgiven for. *(takes a breath)* That's how unforgiving she was.

Selena: So? People still haven't forgiven me for missing that last shot.

Narrator: Nobody's mentioned the game to you since *(flips through script)* Scene Two.

Selena: Because I'm not giving them the chance! I'm not forgiving them before they can not forgive me.

Narrator: O. Kay.

Scene Six

Narrator: *(as other kids and Mrs. Ortez enter)* Selena finally went over the top in art class.

Mrs. Ortez: Your paintings for the contest are due at the end of period. So everybody get busy!

Selena: Just a few more touches, and my painting will be ready.

Caitlyn: That's great. You know, Selena, today—

Selena: I need to get some water for my paints.

Caitlyn: You can share with me.

Selena: No, thanks. I'll get my own.

Narrator: Selena had just filled her cup at the sink when she heard something awful.

Caitlyn: Oops! Oh, no! I can't believe I did that! Oh, this is terrible!

Narrator: Selena rushed back to the table to find that—

Selena: What happened? Oh, no!

Narrator: She found that Caitlyn—

Selena: You clumsy idiot! You've ruined my painting!

Narrator: *(quickly)* She found that Caitlyn had spilled water all over her painting.

Caitlyn: I'm so sorry, Selena! It was an accident.

Selena: I could have won the contest. Now you've ruined everything for me!

Caitlyn: I'm really, really sorry. Please forgive me!

Selena: Never! Never! And what I mean is … never! I can never forgive you!

Caitlyn: *(upset)* I'm sorry! *(exits)*

Mrs. Ortez: Everyone go on with your work while I see what's wrong with Caitlyn. *(exits)*

Mitch: *(to Selena)* How can you act like that?

Frannie: That was just mean.

Tasha: You made her cry.

Pablo: You're cold.

Jake: Sheesh! Are you made of stone?

Selena: No!

Jake: Well, your heart sure is. You don't forgive anybody for anything.

Selena: Why should I?

Tasha: Because … because not forgiving people hurts them!

Selena: You mean … like when somebody makes a mistake and everybody jumps all over them and won't forgive them so they feel cursed for life because they did one little thing wrong? You mean like that?

Tasha: *(muttering)* Not exactly.

Jake: We don't know what you're talking about.

Selena: Right.

Narrator: *(as others exit)* Selena told herself she didn't care that Caitlyn got her feelings hurt. And she told herself she didn't care that everybody was mad at her.

Selena: Look! I'm not just "telling myself" I don't care. I really don't care, OK?

Narrator: Right.

Selena: Well, I don't.

Scene Seven

Narrator: The last period of the day was English. Selena was glad when Mr. Donahue gave a reading assignment with a worksheet.

Selena: Good! I don't have to deal with anybody.

Narrator: But when she saw that the story was titled "Saint Bakhita and the Power of Forgiveness," her heart sank. Forgiveness was kind of a sore subject for Selena.

Selena: My heart isn't sunken at all.

Narrator: To read about forgiveness when her own lack of forgiveness had hurt a dear friend? I mean … talk about an uncomfortable subject!

Selena: I'm not uncomfortable. I haven't done anything wrong. I just treated people the way they treated me. Now be quiet so I can read.

Narrator: Selena found out that Saint Bakhita had an amazing life. When she was a little girl in Africa, she was kidnapped by slave traders. They treated her badly and teased her by giving her the name "Bakhita," which means "lucky one." Then they—

Selena: Trying to read here!

Narrator: *(more quietly)* Poor Bakhita was sold into slavery. For years, she knew nothing but hard work and cruel punishment.

Selena: Her first owner beat her when she accidentally broke a vase. She was just a little kid!

Narrator: She was sold several times, but her life did not get better. Finally, she came into the hands of a couple who took her to Italy to be the caretaker of their little girl. Bakhita loved the child and raised her with kindness. When the girl was older, Bakhita went away to Catholic boarding school with her. Bakhita learned about God from the sisters there.

Selena: And when it was time for the family to return to Africa, Bakhita refused to leave with them. She became a Christian and a religious sister, and she spent the rest of her life doing God's work. She was kind and loving and helpful and … *(quietly)* forgiving.

Narrator: What was that?

Selena: *(louder)* She was really forgiving. I can't believe it! People were so awful to her. I mean … she was kidnapped … and beaten … and mistreated in so many ways … and yet she forgave them all! She said she would have never come to know God without them. That's amazing!

Narrator: It sure is.

Selena: And I couldn't forgive people for … well … I guess it started out because I couldn't forgive them for their remarks about the basketball game. But then I didn't forgive anything at all. I … I was just terrible to my friends!

Narrator: What are you going to do?

Selena: I have to try to make things right. I hope *they* can forgive *me*.

Scene Eight

Narrator: That night Selena called her friends to apologize.

Selena: *(dials)* Hi, Jake! Listen, I … He hung up! *(dials)* Tasha, this is … She hung up, too! I'll try Caitlyn. *(dials)* Hi, Mrs. Moore. Is Caitlyn … ? She doesn't feel well? … Oh. Bye. *(to self)* Nobody will speak to me, but I can't blame them.

Narrator: At school the next morning, she tried again, but no one would even look at her.

Selena: *(looking offstage)* Hi, Frannie! Please don't walk away … Mitch! Mitch! … Hey, Pablo, can I … Are you feeling better, Caitlyn? Caitlyn? … This is awful! I've ruined everything!

Narrator: *(as others enter)* The other kids had to sit with Selena in social studies, but they didn't have to pay attention to her.

Jake: I researched Roosevelt's family. Did you know he was related to another president?

Selena: That's really interesting, Jake. It's Teddy Roosevelt, right?

Frannie: I read about that. Franklin Roosevelt was related to Teddy Roosevelt, wasn't he?

Jake: Right.

Pablo: That's interesting. Let's include it in our report.

Caitlyn: And I found out about Roosevelt's childhood.

Selena: His family was pretty well off, weren't they?

Caitlyn: His family was pretty well off. His father was—

Selena: You guys!

Mitch: Hey, I think I heard something.

Jake: You mean like an annoying little buzzing sound?

Tasha: Let's just ignore it.

Selena: Please just listen to me. I'm trying to apologize.

Caitlyn: Well, hurry it up. We have a lot to do here.

Selena: I'm sorry, OK? Really sorry. Really, really, really sorry.

Jake: And I suppose you expect us to forgive you.

Selena: Not ... not really. I know I was awful to everybody. *(to Jake)* You didn't mean to make more work. *(to Tasha)* And the math paper wasn't a big deal. *(to Mitch)* And you did get to that pizza before I did. I should have forgiven all of you. I was so harsh ... and ... *(whispers)* I'm sorry.

Caitlyn: Well ... we're sorry, too.

Jake: We are?

Pablo: What are you talking about?

Caitlyn: We weren't very forgiving either. About Selena's last shot.

Others: *(mutter)*

Caitlyn: You know we weren't!

Jake: *(muttering)* We were just joking.

Frannie: *(muttering)* Kind of.

Mitch: It was a big game, OK?

Tasha: And we hated to lose.

Jake: But ... but we shouldn't have ganged up on her. That wasn't right.

Others: *(mutter)*

Caitlyn: We hurt her feelings, you guys, and that's why she acted the way she did. *(to Selena)* Not that that's an excuse.

Selena: I know! It's just that forgiving is hard. And I'm not very good at it. But I can do better.

Jake: Do you think you could start by forgiving us?

Tasha: Yeah. We're sorry about how we treated you. Right, you guys?

Others: Yeah. We sure are. *Etc.*

Selena: Sure, I can! But can you all forgive me?

Others: Sure! You bet! OK! *Etc.*

Selena: Thanks! Thanks, you guys!

Narrator: So Selena—

Selena: I'm going to change. I promise!

Narrator: So she decided to—

Selena: It won't be easy. I know that. But I'm really going to try.

Narrator: *(quickly)* So she decided to follow Saint Bakhita's lead and be more forgiving.

Selena: Yeah. I'm going to give it my best shot.

SAINT BAKHITA

Fear Doesn't Scare Me!

SUMMARY

Enrique is shocked to discover his friend, Julian, is a big chicken. Enrique tries to make Julian change, but it's hopeless! Then Enrique has to face fear himself. The story of the Annunciation helps him deal with his own fear—and help his friend, too.

COSTUMES/SETS/PROPS

All actors wear contemporary clothing.

A few tables and chairs or desks can serve as the classrooms and cafeteria.

Actors can pretend their scripts are the play scripts. The Narrator can use a Bible in Scene Eight. Other props can be mimed, but if desired, the following can be used: school books and supplies, cafeteria trays, a kickboard, and a playground ball.

PRESENTATION

The Narrator tries to sound serious but often forgets and slips into a normal voice.

In Scene Three, students can "study" as Enrique, Julian, and Amber talk about the play.

In Scene Four, students "write" on the air as they demonstrate the math problems.

In the last scene, Enrique mimes hitting the ball, acting like a champion, flinching and shrugging, and congratulating Julian. Julian mimes cheering Enrique on, trembling on stage, hearing he got the part, and accepting Enrique's congratulations.

CAST

Narrator

Enrique

Julian

Other students: Amber, Spring, Drew, JJ

Ms. Daniels, the study hall teacher

Mrs. Archer, the math teacher

Coach Whiffle, the PE teacher

ABOUT MARY AND THE ANNUNCIATION

On the day that Jesus began to grow in Mary's womb, God had sent the angel Gabriel to announce the news. Gabriel appeared to Mary in her home in Nazareth, greeted her, and told her that God had blessed her. Then he explained she was to be the mother of Jesus, the Son of God. Mary must have been overwhelmed, but she trusted in the Lord. She courageously accepted his will for her and began her life as the Mother of God. We celebrate this special day on March 25.

Fear Doesn't Scare Me!

Scene One

Narrator: *(serious)* Fear. We've all experienced it. We all fear it. Yes, we all fear fear, but—

Enrique: *(entering)* Fear doesn't scare me. I'm not afraid of anything.

Narrator: *(normal)* What? I mean … *(serious)* Everyone is afraid of something … everyone.

Enrique: OK, I *am* afraid of stuff I should be afraid of. I don't handle hot pots without an oven mitt. And I don't play in traffic. And when my mom yells my whole name, I come running. But that's just normal stuff. Other than that *(mocking Narrator)* I fear nothing.

Narrator: Are you making fun of me?

Enrique: Look … all I'm saying is I'm not some namby-pamby, chicken-hearted, lily-livered, scaredy-cat kind of a person. Like some people!

Narrator: Which brings us to today's story. Enrique had been friends with Julian for a good while, and he thought he knew him well. But one fateful day, Enrique found out the awful truth: Julian really *was* a namby-pamby, chicken-hearted, lily-livered, scaredy-cat kind of a person.

Enrique: Who knew?

Scene Two

Narrator: *(as Julian, Amber enter)* It all started with the morning announcements. *(in a different voice)* Today's lunch will be *(static)* served with fresh *(static)*.

Julian: Mmmm … fresh *(static)*.

Narrator: Play auditions *(static)* on the twenty-fifth at *(static)*. Pick up scripts from *(long static)* ... a nice *(static)*!

Amber: Auditions? In elementary school, the teachers assigned the parts. I liked that better.

Enrique: Of course! They always gave you a leading role. Julian and I got stuck playing the extra Pilgrims in the background.

Julian: I liked being an extra Pilgrim.

Enrique: We never got to talk! But that's not happening this time, Julian, because we're trying out for the biggest roles, and we're going to be stars!

Julian: But if you're a star, you have to talk. In front of everybody. And they listen to you.

Amber: That's what audiences do, all right.

Julian: Well, I don't need that kind of pressure, OK?

Enrique: Gee, Julian. You sound like you're scared. *(laughs)* Wait. You *are* scared, aren't you?

Amber: Plays are fun, Julian.

Julian: When you don't have to say anything! I mean ... when you don't have lines to memorize.

Enrique: But you're good at memorizing. Man. You're really scared! I can't believe it!

Julian: I'm not scared, OK?

Enrique: So you're not afraid to try out for the play?

Julian: No. Of course not.

Enrique: OK then. Let's pick up some scripts. It's time to meet our destiny and become the stars we were always meant to be!

Amber: *(to Julian)* OK. Now *I'm* scared. Of him!

Julian: Heh. Heh. Yeah. Funny. *(serious)* Me, too.

Scene Three

Narrator: *(as Ms. Daniels and other students enter)* So the kids got their scripts and took them to their first-period study hall.

Ms. Daniels: Get to work, everyone! No talking!

Students: Yes, ma'am.

Enrique: OK. What part do you want, Julian?

Julian: I'd like to be … the guard.

Enrique: But the guard doesn't say anything. You don't want a part like that.

Julian: Sure I do. The guard is real … um … tough. I like that.

Enrique: Come on! You should try out for the prince.

Julian: I'm not really the princely type.

Enrique: Sure you are! Isn't he, Amber?

Amber: Huh? I mean … sure. You're very princely.

Julian: Thanks, but I like the guard's part better.

Enrique: You're afraid to try out for the prince, aren't you?

Julian: Of course not! I told you. I don't like to memorize a lot of lines.

Enrique: Right. You're not chicken or anything.

Julian: No, I'm not.

Enrique: Buck-buck-buckaw!

Ms. Daniels: No talking! I mean it!

Students: Yes, ma'am.

Julian: We'd better just study the scripts silently. I don't want to get into trouble.

Enrique: But Ms. Daniels never sends anyone to the office. Hey, are you afraid of her, too?

Julian: No! I'm not afraid of anything!

Ms. Daniels: Julian, you quiet down right now.

Julian: Yes, ma'am. Sorry! I'm so sorry. It won't happen again.

Enrique: *(as Ms. Daniels exits)* Man. You really need help.

Scene Four

Narrator: *(as Mrs. Archer enters)* In math, Julian acted even chickener.

Mrs. Archer: Who can come to the board and solve the first problem?

Everyone except Julian: I'll do it! Pick me! Ooh! *Etc.*

Mrs. Archer: OK ... Drew. Show us how it's done.

Narrator: So Drew demonstrated the first problem, then sat down.

Mrs. Archer: Very good! Now who would like to do the second problem?

Everyone except Julian: I'll do it! Pick me! Ooh! *Etc.*

Mrs. Archer: Amber!

Narrator: Amber solved the second problem, then sat down.

Mrs. Archer: OK, how about problem three?

Everyone except Julian: I'll do it! Pick me! Ooh! *Etc.*

Narrator: *(as kids continue to beg)* OK, so you get the idea. Every time the teacher ... *(to kids)* Excuse me! I'm trying to narrate here. *(when it's quiet)* So whenever the teacher asked for a volunteer, everybody tried to get chosen. Everybody ... except ... Julian.

Enrique: *(to Julian)* You know how to do this stuff. Why aren't you volunteering?

Julian: Why bother?

Enrique: Maybe because Mrs. Archer gives mucho bonus points for class participation?

Julian: Whatever.

Enrique: Now that I think about it, you never volunteer in class.

Julian: Sure I do. When I'm in the mood.

Enrique: Don't, man. Don't tell me you're scared of talking in class. Please don't tell me that.

Julian: OK. I won't.

Narrator: But Enrique felt sure Julian really was afraid.

Enrique: He's scared of everything—and I never knew it!

Scene Five

Narrator: *(as other exit)* Enrique was upset about Julian's chickenness.

Enrique: I have to help him. He can't go through life quaking in his boots over every little thing.

Narrator: So Enrique tried reasoning with Julian ...

Enrique: Look, you dope! It's stupid to be afraid of talking in front of people. They're just people. Does it make sense to be scared of people? Well, duh ... no!

Julian: I'm. Not. Scared.

Narrator: And he tried toughening Julian up ...

Enrique: BOO!

Julian: What did you do that for?

Enrique: I'm just trying ... BOO!

Julian: Stop that!

Enrique: See, I figure you can get used to fear. It's like ... BOO! Hey, it's working! You hardly even flinched that time.

Julian: Give me a break.

Narrator: Most of all, he tried to embarrass Julian into manning up ...

Enrique: *(as other kids enter)* Why aren't you eating your carrots, Julian? You're not ... afraid of them, are you?

Julian: That's ridiculous!

Enrique: So is being scared of class participation.

Julian: I'm not!

Enrique: Right. That's why you never raise your hand.

Spring: Maybe he doesn't raise his hand because he doesn't know the answer.

Enrique: Or maybe it's because he's a big chicken. Buck-buck-buckaw!

Julian: I am not!

Enrique: Hey, everybody, who's the most not-scary teacher in school?

Amber: Mr. Gaston.

Enrique: No!

Spring: Senora Yablonski.

Enrique: Are you kidding?

Drew: Coach Whiffle.

Enrique: It's Ms. Daniels. You'd have to be a complete and total chicken to be afraid of her.

Others: Yeah. Right. *Etc.*

Enrique: Can you believe Julian is scared to death of Ms. Daniels?

JJ: She's really nice, dude. You don't have to be afraid.

Julian: I'm! Not!

Enrique: Of course not. *(quietly)* Buck-buck-buckaw!

Narrator: Julian kept claiming he wasn't afraid of anything. But Enrique knew better.

Enrique: *(as others exit)* I never realized it before, but he is the chickenest person I've ever known. Sometimes he even tries to run away from *me*. He has a real problem!

Narrator: He sure does.

Scene Six

Narrator: Enrique just wouldn't let up on Julian.

Enrique: *(as Julian enters)* I have to get him cured of his problem before the play tryouts.

Narrator: And finally Julian couldn't take it anymore.

Julian: If you cluck at me one more time, I'm going to clobber you!

Enrique: *(amused)* Come on, Julian. We both know *that's* not happening.

Julian: Because I'm a big chicken?

Enrique: Hey, if the feathers fit …

Julian: OK, I'll admit I'm scared of performing on stage. That much is true. But I'm not frightened of everything in the whole world, Enrique!

Enrique: Look. I understand. You're afraid to face the truth about yourself …

Julian: That's it! That! Is! It! Our friendship is over! *(exits)*

Enrique: Well … I tried. It's terrible when someone has a big personality flaw and can't see it.

Narrator: Are you kidding me? I mean … *(serious)* Yes. Yes, it is.

Scene Seven

Narrator: *(as Coach Whiffle and students enter)* Our story might have ended right there but for one compelling and significant change in Enrique's life: his first encounter with … boogie ball.

Coach Whiffle: Listen up! Boogie ball is just like baseball. Except there are no baseballs. Or bats. Or bases. Other than that, it's just like baseball.

JJ: OK, I'm confused.

Coach Whiffle: Listen up! Instead of a bat, we'll use this old kickboard.

Spring: What *is* that?

Enrique: It's for the pool. You know … you lie down on it and kick back and forth.

Drew: Oh. Yeah.

Coach Whiffle: Listen up! Instead of a baseball, we'll use this playground ball. Instead of bases, we'll use marks on the gym floor. Other than that, boogie ball is just like baseball. Except we can play it inside in bad weather. OK, Team A! You're up to bat!

Enrique: Shouldn't that be "up to boogie"?

Narrator: While Enrique was … boogie-ing … it happened. The thing that would forever change his attitude about fear. He blinked, and BAM! he got smacked in the face with the boogie ball.

Enrique: YEEEEOWWW!

Spring: Are you OK?

Drew: Did you break your nose?

JJ: Is that a foul?

Narrator: Coach Whiffle sent Enrique to the nurse. Luckily, he was just fine. But the next day in PE, Enrique couldn't get a single hit because he kept flinching away from the pitches. We're talking major flinching. Like the really obvious kind of flinching that is so-o-o embarrassing.

JJ: Are you scared of the ball?

Enrique: No!

Amber: Everybody's afraid of stuff sometimes, Enrique. You don't have to pretend.

Enrique: I'm not pretending. I'm fine. I'm not afraid of some stupid plastic ball.

Narrator: Enrique felt he had to say that stuff, especially since Julian was standing right there. But the truth was that he now knew fear. And he feared it. What if everybody figured out *he* was a namby-pamby, chicken-hearted, lily-livered, scaredy-cat kind of a person?

Enrique: That can never happen. Never!

Scene Eight

Narrator: *(as others exit)* Over the next few days, Enrique avoided playing boogie ball by pretending to be sick or injured. He felt terrible about the deception, but ...

Enrique: If I get up there and make a fool of myself again, everybody will know I'm afraid.

Narrator: Being afraid was a lot harder than Enrique ever imagined.

Enrique: Yeah. It's really pretty scary. I shouldn't have been so hard on Julian.

Narrator: He thought about talking to Julian and telling him he now understood, but ...

Enrique: He might figure out I'm a chicken, too. I can't let him find out the truth!

Narrator: *(quietly)* Buck-buck!

Enrique: What was that?

Narrator: Being afraid was just terrible. Living in fear of fear. Scared of being scared. Chicken of looking like a chicken. Things seemed hopeless until the day of the play tryouts. It was also the feast of the Annunciation, so there was Mass first thing in the morning. The Gospel reading was from Luke, chapter 1, verses 26 to 38. That's when Enrique noticed something different about the story of the Annunciation.

Enrique: It's cool how the angel Gabriel tells Mary she's going to be the Mother of God.

Narrator: *(reading)* "The angel greeted Mary and said, 'You are truly blessed! The Lord is with you.' Mary was confused by the angel's words and wondered what they meant."

Enrique: *(to self)* Yeah, I guess so! If an angel suddenly appeared to me, I'd freak out! I mean ... I'd be so afraid.

Narrator: "Then the angel told Mary, 'Don't be afraid! God is pleased with you, and you will have a son. His name will be Jesus.'"

Enrique: I'll bet Mary *was* scared. How could she not be with an angel standing there? And when she found out she was having a baby, she probably got more scared. And the baby would be the Son of God! How scary is that? She must have been terrified that she couldn't handle it.

Narrator: "Mary said, 'I am the Lord's servant! Let it happen as you have said.' "

Enrique: Man. That's courage.

Narrator: After the service, Enrique couldn't stop thinking about Mary.

Enrique: She was afraid. But she trusted God to get her through everything. Hey, I just realized something!

Narrator: That it's really strange the way you keep talking to the narrator of the play?

Enrique: No. … Wai-ait. That is … Never mind! I realized that being brave is doing something *even though* you're scared. And there's only one way to get through something that hard! Man. If only I'd known that before, I could have really helped Julian.

Narrator: Maybe it's not too late.

Enrique: Maybe.

Scene Nine

Narrator: All the next day, Enrique thought about talking to Julian. But it's not easy to face up to somebody you've treated badly.

Enrique: He'll never want to be my friend again. But maybe he'll listen to me one more time.

Narrator: *(as Julian enters)* Finally, just before PE, Enrique got the guts to face Julian.

Enrique: Hey, can I talk to you?

Julian: Is there going to be any clucking?

Enrique: No! I promise!

Julian: All right.

Enrique: I just wanted to say I'm sorry for how I acted. I wasn't understanding at all, but now I get it and … I'm really sorry.

Julian: OK. Is that it?

Enrique: No. There's one more thing. Now I can actually help you with your fear. See, all you—

Julian: I knew it! I knew it! You don't understand anything at all!

Enrique: Yes, I do! Because *(mutters)*.

Julian: What?

Enrique: I'm scared of something now, OK? I'm . . . I'm a chicken!

Julian: You are?

Enrique: Yes, I am. Buck-buck-buckaw!

Julian: *(seriously)* I thought you said there wouldn't be any clucking.

Enrique, Julian: *(look at each other and crack up)*

Enrique: Seriously. I know how to help both of us handle our fears. Just listen.

Julian: OK.

Enrique: *(takes a big breath)* Buck-buck-buck. Buck-buckaw!

Enrique, Julian: *(crack up)*

Enrique: OK. For real now.

Narrator: Enrique explained how he had been inspired by Mary's courage.

Enrique: We have to trust God, too—just like Mary did. If we ask him to help us, he'll give us the strength to face the stuff that scares us.

Julian: *(teasing)* Stuff like boogie balls?

Enrique: Man, that's not what really scares me. I mean . . . when the ball is coming at me, yeah, I'm scared. But I'm *really* afraid about what everyone will think of me.

Julian: I know. It's rough when people think you're a chicken.

Enrique: I'm really sorry, Julian. I shouldn't have assumed you were afraid of everything.

Julian: Well. I *am* a little afraid of Ms. Daniels.

Drew: *(entering)* The coach said you're up to bat, Enrique. Come on! *(exits)*

Julian: You'll be all right.

Scene Ten

Narrator: *(as Enrique and Julian mime)* So Enrique hit a grand-slam boogie ball, becoming the star of his team. Eventually, he earned a boogie ball scholarship to a major college where he … *(normal)* OK. He flinched. Every time he went up to boogie. He took a lot of teasing about that. But he asked God to help him through it, and usually he handled things pretty well. *(serious)* And what about Julian? He, too, found that trusting God helped him handle his fears. He was terrified, but he auditioned for a small speaking part. *(normal)* And he got it!

Julian: *(exiting)* I can't wait to tell my parents!

Narrator: *(serious)* So … we all know fear. And we all fear it. Yes, we all fear fear, and yet we—

Enrique: Hey, fear doesn't scare me.

Narrator: *(annoyed)* Dude, did you learn absolutely nothing?

Enrique: Let me finish! Fear doesn't scare me … as much as it used to. Now I think about Mother Mary—and trust in God. I might still feel afraid, but I can get through it with God's help.

Narrator: Oh. OK then. You did learn something. So I guess our work here is finished.

Enrique: *(as they exit)* So … about this talking to the narrator thing …

MARY,
THE MOTHER OF GOD

Plenty of Time

SUMMARY

Asia loves her active life, but everybody else thinks she's too busy with things that don't matter. Asia rearranges her activities to fit in more of the important stuff, but the new schedule just doesn't work. Could she change her life by setting priorities as Saint Gianna Molla did?

COSTUMES/SETS/PROPS

All characters wear contemporary clothing. Asia, Meadow, and Rick could have karate outfits for Scene One.

A table and chairs can represent Asia's kitchen and bedroom, school, and the youth group meeting room. In Scene One, chairs can be set up two by two to suggest a car.

Davis needs a book about the saints, or his script can be covered to look like such a book. If other props are desired, the following can be used: dishes and utensils, some papers for Asia to give to Paul in Scene Three, and schoolbooks.

PRESENTATION

In Scene Five, Asia can "hang" her big calendar between herself and the audience and mime writing on it.

CAST

Narrator

Asia

Dad and Mom, Asia's parents

Davis, Asia's older brother

Asia's friends, Meadow and Rick

Other youth group kids: Laurie, Paul, and extra kids, if desired

Ms. Steiner, youth group sponsor

ABOUT SAINT GIANNA MOLLA

In 1922, Gianna was born into a large, devout Italian family. Her upbringing gave her a strong faith. She became a doctor to help others as Jesus did, and she gave generously of her time to the poor, the elderly, the sick, and others in need. When she married, she dedicated herself to being a good wife and mother as well. When she was pregnant with her fourth child, she developed a tumor in her uterus. She risked her life by refusing an abortion and asking doctors to remove only the tumor. Later, when the baby was ready to be delivered, she again asked doctors to save the child even if that meant she herself would die. Her baby daughter was born safely. Gianna survived the birth but developed a serious infection and died a week later at only 39 years old. Her feast day is April 28. Saint Gianna is the patron of mothers and physicians.

Plenty of Time

Scene One

Narrator: Nobody was as busy as Asia. If she wasn't doing homework, she was attending a club meeting. When there wasn't a meeting, she had some kind of lesson. If she didn't have a lesson, she practiced something. Whenever she caught up on practicing, she updated her blog. If her blog was current, she did homework. If her homework . . . Well, anyway . . . Asia was very busy.

Asia: There are just so many things I like to do!

Narrator: *(as Asia's family enters)* Some people thought Asia was *too* busy. Like her family.

Dad: Supper's ready!

Asia: I already ate a sandwich. And now I have to get to karate.

Mom: But I thought we'd have a nice meal together tonight.

Davis: Come on! Couldn't you just skip for once?

Asia: And disappoint Sensei McNamara? I don't think so.

Mom: Well, we're just sitting down to eat, so nobody can take you to karate right now.

Asia: That's OK. I'm getting a ride with Meadow. See you later!

Narrator: *(as family exits, shaking their heads, and Meadow, Rick, and Mrs. Franklin enter)* Asia's friends also thought she was too busy.

Asia: Hi! Thanks for the ride, Mrs. Franklin. I really appreciate it.

Mrs. Franklin: You're welcome, dear.

Meadow: Hey, you guys! Mom's taking us out for ice cream after karate.

Rick: Thanks, Mrs. Franklin.

Asia: I'm sorry, but I have a singing lesson after karate. Could you drop me off?

Mrs. Franklin: Sure, Asia.

Rick: Didn't you have a singing lesson yesterday?

Asia: Yeah, but that was a make-up for the time I missed when French Club had that dinner to raise money for our museum trip, which made me miss gymnastics so I had to reschedule that during the time I would've had singing. This is my real lesson tonight.

Rick: O. Kay.

Meadow: You never have time to do anything with us, Asia! Couldn't you just not go tonight?

Asia: And let my amazing God-given vocal talent go to waste?

Rick: Sheesh! How much are you paying that singing teacher?

Asia: What do mean by that?

Mrs. Franklin: Oh, look! We're here!

Narrator: *(as others exit)* The only person who didn't think Asia was too busy was Asia.

Asia: It's good to be home! Now I just have to do my math, draw a poster for the Art Club bake sale, oh! bake some cookies, and add to my blog. Wow! This sure has been a slow day.

Scene Two

Narrator: Asia liked the idea of living a full life, and she didn't understand why people kept complaining. She felt she spent plenty of time with everybody—even her brother.

Davis: *(entering)* OK, I checked this book about the saints out of the library.

Asia: Because ... ?

Davis: Remember? You said you'd help me choose my confirmation name?

Asia: Oh, yeah. Well ... um ... I don't need that book. I think you should pick the name "John."

Davis: Really? Which John did you have in mind?

Asia: You know ... Saint ... John.

Davis: Which Saint John?

Asia: Um … Saint John of *(mumble)*.

Davis: Oh, I get it. You don't have time for me in your crazy schedule so you're blowing me off.

Asia: That's not true! I just really like Saint John. I mean … *all* of the Saint Johns.

Dad: *(entering)* Asia, we'd better get you to your youth group meeting.

Asia: OK, Dad. Thanks. *(Dad exits)*

Davis: So I guess we're finished here. Gee, thanks a million, Sis.

Asia: You're welcome. I'm always glad to help.

Davis: *(exits muttering)*

Asia: What's he so grouchy about? If he didn't want my opinion, he shouldn't have asked for it!

Scene Three

Narrator: *(as Meadow, Rick, and youth group enter)* Asia was always there for her friends, too.

Meadow: I have to talk to you. Brittany's been gossiping about me!

Asia: That's awful! Oh, hi, Laurie. Could we meet tomorrow morning and fold those flyers?

Laurie: Sure.

Asia: Great. See you then.

Meadow: So anyway she said I cheated—

Asia: Paul! Here's my part of the social studies outline.

Paul: Thanks.

Meadow: But I wouldn't—

Asia: There's Jen. I have to find out what happened at—

Meadow: Asia! I'm trying to talk to you about a problem.

Asia: And I am here for you. Just let me talk to Jen for two seconds. Then I'll be right back.

Meadow: Don't bother.

Asia: Oh. So you were done with your story?

Meadow: Yeah. I'm done all right.

Asia: OK. Well, just remember ... I care.

Meadow: Are you kidding?

Asia: No. Why would you think that?

Meadow: Maybe because you don't care about anything except your ridiculous schedule?

Asia: Not that again! Look, Meadow, I'm sorry I'm so busy, but I spend as much time with you as I can. My life is about more than just you, OK?

Meadow: I'm not saying—

Asia: I guess I could give up all the things I do for other people. Then I'd have plenty of extra time just for you.

Meadow: Right. Like what ... five minutes on Thursday?

Asia: Look, I have to talk to Jen before the meeting starts.

Meadow: Go ahead. Take your time.

Scene Four

Narrator: *(as Ms. Steiner enters)* Asia was tired of everybody criticizing her, but what happened at youth group that night *did* make her think.

Ms. Steiner: Who can work at the meal center on Saturday?

Other kids: I can! Me! I'll be there! *Etc.*

Asia: I'm sorry, Ms. Steiner, but this Saturday I'm making up a gymnastics lesson, writing a report, and updating my personal blog. I don't think I can get to the meal center.

Paul: Gee. There's a surprise.

Ms. Steiner: I understand. Maybe you could help at the fish fry the night before.

Asia: *This* Friday? Hmmm ... There's my salsa lesson at four, clarinet at—

Meadow: We get it! You can't help.

Asia: Look, I'd be glad to help if I could. I'm all about helping, OK?

Ms. Steiner: Of course, dear. Maybe you could choose a Scripture passage for our next meeting.

Asia: Um… I'm going to have to miss that one.

Ms. Steiner: Well, could you serve at the seven o'clock Mass one Sunday next month?

Asia: That doesn't work for me.

Ms. Steiner: Visit the—

Asia: Busy.

Ms. Steiner: Make the—

Asia: Nope.

Laurie: Brother.

Ms. Steiner: Can anybody else help with those activities?

Others: Sure! I can! You bet! *Etc.*

Ms. Steiner: Well then … I think that's it for tonight. See you all next week.

Asia: Um… Not me.

Ms. Steiner: Right.

Meadow: *(as others exit)* See? You *are* too busy! You never have time to help with anything.

Asia: OK, I *haven't* helped out much lately. But I can fix that. I'll just rearrange my schedule.

Meadow: I don't think that'll solve the problem, Asia.

Asia: Sure it will. You'll see!

Scene Five

Narrator: *(as Meadow exits)* Asia was sure she could fit more into her schedule.

Asia: I probably waste plenty of time—a few minutes here, a few minutes there. I just have to get rid of any dead time like that. Then I'll be able to do everything I want.

Narrator: So Asia put up a humongous calendar on her bedroom wall and started rearranging her schedule, squishing everything as close together as she could.

Asia: OK! If I move my clarinet lesson ... and take two singing lessons back-to-back ... and put this on Monday... and move that... and voilà! I have free time in my schedule! I have ... *(mutter)*

Narrator: I don't believe the audience heard that.

Asia: I have five minutes free on Thursday, OK? But wait! I'll move this... and take the early dance class on Saturday... and go to that a little late... and voilà! I really *do* have plenty of time in my schedule. Now I can fit in everything—and everybody!

Davis: *(entering)* What are you doing?

Asia: Working on my schedule. I moved things around and found some extra time.

Davis: That's amazing. So can you *really* help me with my confirmation name?

Asia: Sure! And, listen, I'm sorry about before. I wasn't operating at my most efficient then. But now I can help you... let me check my schedule... next Tuesday at five-thirty.

Davis: But that's when my confirmation group is going to the nursing home.

Asia: You're going to the nursing home at five-thirty in the morning?

Davis: In the morning! You expect me to get up before dawn has even cracked to talk to you?

Asia: OK, don't freak! I have plenty of time available like ... two weeks from today at nine pm.

Davis: Never mind! *(exits)*

Asia: Sheesh! Does he expect me to arrange my entire life around *his* schedule?

Scene Six

Narrator: *(as Meadow and Rick enter)* Asia tried to make her new schedule work, but nobody would cooperate—not even her friends.

Asia: Listen, you guys, I'm sorry about how busy I've been. And I've rearranged some things so I'll have more time for you.

Meadow: Wow. I didn't think you could do it.

Rick: That's great. Thanks, Asia.

Asia: So ... meet me outside the pottery studio at six-forty-five on Wednesday. My art class starts at seven, so don't be late or we won't have time to talk before I go in.

Meadow: Excuse me?

Rick: *(sarcastic)* Let me explain, Meadow. Asia is generously offering us a whole fifteen minutes out of her busy life so we'd better rearrange our schedules so we can be there at the assigned time or we'll miss a heart-warming moment of true friendship. *(to Asia)* Right?

Asia: I don't know that we'll have time for anything *really* heart-warming, but I—

Meadow: Well, I can't make it.

Rick: Me neither.

Asia: Oh, OK. How about Thursday at—

Meadow: Can't make it.

Rick: Nope.

Asia: Three weeks from Friday I could—

Meadow: Busy.

Rick: Yeah, busy.

Asia: You know, I rearranged my schedule for you guys!

Meadow: Sorry. It just doesn't work for me.

Rick: Or me.

Asia: *(as they exit)* When did they get so busy?

Scene Seven

Narrator: Asia stuck to the new schedule, but her family and friends were almost never available during the times she set aside for them. And her youth group activities usually didn't fit those slots either, so she wasn't helping out much more than she did before. And she was *always* running late for something or leaving early or playing catch-up. One night, she came home exhausted and finally admitted the truth.

Asia: I'm too busy! But how can that be when I have such a perfect schedule? I should have plenty of time for everything.

Davis: *(entering)* You're late.

Asia: For what?

Davis: Sheesh! Remember two weeks ago when you said we could meet at nine tonight?

Asia: But I thought you didn't want to do that. I didn't put you on my schedule.

Davis: Oh, great. You're never going to help me, are you? You know, while I was waiting for this … appointment … I read the whole book about the saints. You could learn a thing or two about handling a busy schedule from Saint Gianna Molla.

Asia: Right. Like some old saint could possibly have been as busy as I am.

Davis: She wasn't old! She was a young wife and mother. And she was way busy. She was a doctor. And she helped the poor. And she volunteered a lot. And she—

Asia: OK, OK! She was great. So make *her* your confirmation saint.

Davis: Look, I really wanted your ideas about my confirmation name, but I can figure that out for myself. When are *you* going to figure things out, Asia? Your life is a mess!

Asia: It's not that bad! I just have to work the bugs out of my schedule.

Davis: You tried that already, and you're busier than ever!

Asia: Well, things will get better. Hey … how did Saint Gianna do it all?

Davis: I guess she was able to work things out because she loved God so much. Doing God's will every day was like her top priority.

Asia: *(mumbling)* I'm good with God.

Davis: Yeah, but is he your top priority?

Asia: Yes! *(muttering)* When I have time. *(normal)* Anyway … a lot of what I do is just stuff. It's not about God.

Davis: Saint Gianna tried to make *everything* about God. She had a really active prayer life, for one thing. And she became a doctor because she wanted to follow Jesus and help people. She saw Jesus in everyone so she got involved in organizations that cared for the poor. And she believed babies were a gift from God. So when she needed an operation while she was pregnant, she told the doctors to save the baby— even if that meant she herself would die.

Asia: She sounds amazing. Really. But I'll bet her schedule was nothing like mine. She didn't have salsa lessons and French Club and karate and all that stuff clogging up *her* schedule!

Davis: Of course she didn't! Haven't you been listening? Saint Gianna set some priorities in her life. You could do that, too, if you'd only … oh, never mind! *(exits)*

Asia: *(snorts)* Like I have time for priorities.

Scene Eight

Narrator: After Davis left, Asia updated her blog, but Saint Gianna kept coming to her mind.

Asia: I wish I could be like Saint Gianna, but my life is nothing like hers. Well … except the being busy part. And … and I love God, of course. Maybe I don't focus on him as much as she did, but, hey, I'm just an ordinary person living an ordinary life. A very *busy*, ordinary life.

Narrator: Later Asia tried to study, but she just couldn't concentrate.

Asia: I'd love to help other people like Saint Gianna did. And I would if I had plenty of time. But I'm just too busy!

Narrator: Then Asia put aside her schoolwork and practiced karate awhile. But she still couldn't stop thinking about Saint Gianna.

Asia: *(while kicking and chopping)* So maybe … I'm not exactly … devoted to my family … like she was … but I spend … as much … time with them … as I … can!

Narrator: Just before going to bed, Asia took a look at her calendar. And her heart sank.

Asia: If I'm late for karate again tomorrow, Sensei McNamara's going to be mad, but French Club will probably run over, and then I won't have time to practice my clarinet, and I'm going to completely miss the youth group's trip to the children's home and … AARGH! I'll bet even Saint Gianna couldn't handle my schedule! I'll bet she wouldn't even *try!*

Narrator: And that's when Asia realized something.

Asia: Of course, she wouldn't try. Duh. Like she would use up her time on lessons when she could be with her family. Or get involved in so many clubs she couldn't be a good doctor. Or let the computer keep her from helping the poor. I mean … if they'd had computers back then. She used the time God gave her for doing what really mattered—the things he wanted her to do.

Narrator: Asia took a long, hard look at the activities on her crowded schedule.

Asia: I've been acting like everything matters just the same as everything else! But that's not true. Some things are more important than others. And there's only so much time in a day. Shouldn't I be spending most of it on the important things, like Saint Gianna did?

Narrator: It was getting late, but Asia put up a new calendar page and started rescheduling her life. Of course, she had to drop some activities. That was tough.

Asia: I hate to give anything up, but I guess that's what Davis meant about focusing on God and setting priorities. Let's see … I really enjoy singing more than clarinet … and salsa lessons aren't as fun as when I started … And my schoolwork is more important than French club at this point …

Narrator: When she finished, Asia actually had some pretty big blank areas on her calendar.

Asia: Wow! I really think I'm on the right track!

Scene Nine

Narrator: *(as Meadow and Rick enter)* Asia's first few days on her new schedule seemed a bit empty. But soon she realized how nice it was to have time for her friends.

Asia: Hey, do you guys want to come over after school and play some games?

Meadow: Like what? Checker?

Asia: Yeah, we could play checkers.

Meadow: No, I said, "checker." Like we each get one checker. That way we can finish the game before you have to leave.

Asia: Oh, I don't have anywhere to go tonight.

Rick: Seriously?

Asia: Yeah. I cleared a lot of stuff out of my schedule.

Meadow: Seriously?

Asia: Yes. So can you come?

Rick: *(to Meadow)* Is she serious?

Meadow: *(to Rick)* I think so.

Rick: OK! We'll be there.

Asia: Great!

Narrator: *(as Ms. Steiner and youth group kids enter)* And it was wonderful to have the time to get more involved in youth group activities.

Ms. Steiner: Who can help out at the food bank this weekend?

Asia: I can, Ms. Steiner.

Paul: Right. For what? Ten minutes?

Asia: No, I can stay the whole time.

Laurie: Seriously?

Asia: Yes. I changed my schedule so now I have more time to help out.

Paul: *(to Laurie)* Is she joking?

Laurie: *(to Paul)* I don't think so.

Asia: Oh, and I'll be there for our next visit to the children's home.

Ms. Steiner: Seriously? I mean … that's wonderful, Asia.

Narrator: *(as others exit and family enters)* And it was great to spend more time with her family.

Dad: Supper's ready!

Asia: Wow. This looks great, Dad.

Mom: So where do you need to go tonight?

Asia: I'm not going anywhere.

Dad: Are you sick?

Asia: No. I just decided to set priorities in my life and spend more time on what really matters.

Davis: *(teasing)* Gee. Where did you get an idea like that?

Asia: *(teasing)* From a wise and wonderful person!

Davis: You mean … ?

Asia: Yep! Saint Gianna!

Davis: Funny.

Narrator: *(as family exits)* Not that everything was just perfect after that. Sometimes Asia's activities started taking over her life again. When that happened, she thought about Saint Gianna and took a hard look at her own priorities. Keeping her schedule in balance wasn't always easy, but she really tried to stay focused and make time for the important stuff.

Asia: You know, I think I'm going to take "Gianna" for *my* confirmation name.

Narrator: But your confirmation isn't for two more years. You don't have to decide that yet.

Asia: Yeah. I guess not. After all, I have *(grinning)* plenty … of … time.

Saint Gianna Molla

The Mouth

SUMMARY

Tate starts using bad language to impress the other kids. He likes the attention he gets, so he tells himself the way he's talking is OK. So what if he uses some interesting vocabulary? It's not like he's doing anything wrong. Is he?

COSTUMES/SETS/PROPS

All actors can wear contemporary clothing. The coach could wear sweats and sneakers.

A few tables, chairs, or desks can serve as classrooms and the cafeteria.

The following props can be used, if desired: Tate's damaged science project, school books, math quiz in Scene Three, lunch trays, and an English test in Scene Eight.

PRESENTATION

Tate uses the nonsense word *flooglemump* for swear words.

When the Narrator interferes, the other cast members glare or act annoyed.

In Scene Five, the teachers surround Tate. He could do a few push-ups as they exit.

CAST

Narrator

Tate

Tate's friends: Jordan, Eddie, Rose, and Brody

Michael

Hunter

Teachers: Ms. Staley—art, Mrs. Perez—math, Mr. Trudeau—English

Coach Jamison

ABOUT SAINT BERNARDINE OF SIENA

Bernardine was born in Italy in 1380, orphaned at a young age, and raised by relatives. He was a principled boy who despised indecent language, and his friends looked to him as a leader. As a young man, he cared tirelessly for the sick. When he became a Franciscan priest, his weak voice limited his preaching. After he prayed to the Virgin Mary, his voice became strong enough to allow him to preach throughout Italy. Thousands flocked to his sermons, which often focused on the Holy Name of Jesus. Bernardine encouraged the display of the "IHS" symbol that represents Jesus' name. He died in 1444, worn out by his unending efforts to spread the word of God. His feast day is May 20. Saint Bernardine is the patron of advertisers and gambling addicts.

The Mouth

Scene One

Narrator: The first time Tate said ... one of those words ... it sort of just slipped out.

Tate: I spent weeks on that ocean diorama, and then I tripped and dropped it as I was carrying it into the science room and it fell apart. I was mad, OK?

Narrator: And before he knew it, he was saying something he shouldn't.

Tate: *Flooglemump*!

Eddie: Whoa!

Rose: I can't believe you said that!

Brody: I didn't even know you knew that word.

Michael: I didn't know you had the guts to say it.

Jordan: *(to Michael)* You act like you're impressed or something.

Michael: I guess I am ... kind of.

Narrator: Brother! You know it isn't right to. ... *(notices others glaring)* So ... on with the play!

Tate: What am I going to do? We have to turn our projects in today, and mine is a mess!

Eddie: We'll help you fix it.

Others: Yeah. Sure. *Etc.*

Tate: Thanks. Thanks a lot.

Brody: But we don't have time to make it as good as it was.

Rose: Yeah. Your grade's going to be affected.

Tate: Well, *flooglemump*!

Narrator: He-ey! I mean … It's your line, Brody.

Brody: I know. *(to Tate)* I can't believe you said that word again!

Michael: *(admiring)* Dude, you are so bad.

Tate: Um … thanks … I guess.

Scene Two

Narrator: Tate forgot about that little incident until PE.

Jordan: Isn't this the day we're getting tested on our push-ups?

Rose: So? We only have to do twenty of them. That's easy!

Michael: Yeah. I can do twenty with one hand tied behind my back.

Brody: I can do fifty. At least. How many can you do, Tate?

Tate: I don't know.

Eddie: *(snorts)* You only did seven the other day when we were practicing.

Tate: And a half.

Hunter: That is so lame!

Tate: Well … I … I mean …

Narrator: That's when Tate remembered the reaction his language got that morning.

Tate: Look, I don't give a *flooglemump* about any push-ups.

Brody: That's some really bad language, Tate.

Michael: He doesn't care.

Tate: You're *flooglemump* right about that.

Others: *(laugh)*

Hunter: I always thought you were the goody-goody type, Tate, but you're a regular guy.

Tate: *(snorts)* Of course I am.

Scene Three

Narrator: After that, the bad language came easier to Tate. Which is how things like that work. You let yourself do something you shouldn't, and before you know it … *(notices glares)* When Mrs. Perez passed out a pop quiz in math, Tate waited until she moved away. Then he let loose.

Tate: *Flooglemump!*

Michael: I hear you, dude.

Jordan: It's a good thing Mrs. Perez didn't!

Brody: *(muttering)* Too bad we did!

Narrator: *(muttering)* No kidding!

Tate: Aren't you supposed to be narrating?

Narrator: I *am* narrating! *(turning to audience)* And when Tate shut a cabinet door on his finger in art, some more words slipped out.

Tate: *Flooglemump!*

Rose: Are you OK?

Tate: *Flooglemump!*

Eddie: I guess not.

Tate: *Flooglemump!*

Michael: So what are you trying to say?

Tate: I guess what I mean is *flooglemump!*

Others (except Brody): *(laugh)*

Ms. Staley: *(entering)* What's going on over here?

Tate: Nothing, Ms. Staley. *(after she exits)* Just feeling a little *flooglemump!*

Others (except Brody): *(laugh)*

Hunter: You crack me up, dude.

Jordan: But you shouldn't talk like that, Tate.

Tate: Hey, I'll talk however I want.

Narrator: And when Tate saw the Brussels sprouts on his lunch tray, a volcano of bad language erupted out of him.

Tate: *Flooglemump-a-mump!*

Jordan: What's the matter now?

Tate: I hate Brussels sprouts. I mean … I really hate them.

Brody: Well, take it easy. They're only a vegetable.

Tate: They're not just any vegetable, Brody. They're the *flooglemump* of vegetables!

Others (except Brody and Jordan): *(laugh)*

Jordan: Give it a break, Tate.

Narrator: But Tate was enjoying the reaction he got when he cursed. He could see that people were looking at him differently—like he was tougher than they ever thought. And he liked it.

Scene Four

Narrator: Over the next few days, Tate kept displaying his … um … extensive vocabulary.

Tate: Nobody noticed me before, but this whole bad-mouth thing is making me kind of popular.

Narrator: Not that he thought using foul language was right … exactly.

Tate: OK, so there are better words to use, but is it really a big deal? It's not like I'm doing something terrible like lying or stealing. I'm just saying a few interesting words. That's all.

Narrator: But not everybody liked Tate's new personality. *(muttering)* Who can blame them?

Tate: *(to Narrator)* Hey, nobody needs your comments. *(to others)* So this dope knocks my books down. Then he starts to walk away. So I told him to *flooglemumpity-mump!*

Others (except Brody and Jordan): *(laugh)*

Brody: *(to Jordan)* This is getting ridiculous.

Jordan: *(to Brody)* I know! It's just not right.

Tate: What the *flooglemump* are you two mumbling about?

Brody: We're wondering if you can say anything without swearing.

Tate: Well, *flooglemump!* Of course, I can. Oops! I guess not.

Others (except Brody and Jordan): *(laugh)*

Jordan: You're not funny, Tate.

Hunter: What's your problem, Jordan?

Jordan: Nothing. *(exits)*

Brody: Wait up, Jordan! *(exits)*

Michael: Why are they getting so bent out of shape?

Tate: Who the *flooglemump* knows?

Others: *(exit laughing)*

Tate: What difference do a few little words make? Jordan and Brody are making a big deal out of nothing. Who cares how I talk? Sheesh! Like stuff like that matters. Brother.

Scene Five

Narrator: After that, Jordan and Brody started avoiding Tate. Tate told himself he didn't care.

Tate: I think I'm popular enough that I won't miss a couple of goody-goody losers.

Narrator: For a while, Tate didn't think much about his old friends. He was too busy keeping up his new, tough reputation. Which was getting harder to do. *(as Hunter, Michael, Rose, and Eddie enter)* People weren't as easily impressed anymore, so he had to make his language even worse.

Tate: *Flooglemumpity flooglemump!*

Hunter: *(impressed)* You're going to burn that tongue right out of your mouth!

Michael: Hey, I think he fried my eardrums.

Rose: *(aside to Eddie)* What does that stuff he said mean?

Eddie: *(to Rose)* You don't want to know.

Narrator: *(as kids exit and teachers enter)* When Tate wasn't cursing, nobody noticed him, so he had to curse more often. So often that he sometimes got caught by his teachers.

Mrs. Perez: Tate! I will not tolerate that kind of language in my classroom!

Tate: Sorry, Mrs. Perez.

Mr. Trudeau: The English language is a beautiful thing. Please show it some respect.

Tate: Yes, sir. Sorry, sir.

Coach Jamison: Drop and give me fifty push-ups.

Tate: Yes, Coach.

Narrator: *(as teachers exit)* But Tate felt he had to keep cursing. It was part of his image now.

Tate: *(acting tough)* M-hm. I'm bad. That's me. The bad-mouth kid. M-hm.

Coach Jamison: *(entering and surprising Tate)* Tate, I'd like a word with you.

Tate: *(in a squeaky, startled voice)* OK!

Coach Jamison: What's going on with you these days?

Tate: *(still squeaky)* What do you … *(very low)* What do you mean, Coach?

Coach Jamison: I mean your language. You never used to talk like that. And now I hear you're making a habit of it.

Tate: Well … sometimes stuff just slips out. But I'm going to watch my language from now on.

Coach Jamison: God didn't give you the ability to speak so you could fill your mouth with ugliness.

Tate: I … I know.

Coach Jamison: So use clean language. You know … be nice.

Tate: OK. I sure will.

Coach Jamison: Good! *(exits)*

Tate: "Be nice"? Hey, I'm nice. The way I talk doesn't have anything to do with that.

Narrator: But Tate decided maybe he *could* cut back a little on the swearing.

Tate: Like whenever teachers might overhear me!

Scene Six

Narrator: People started calling Tate "The Mouth," which he liked.

Tate: I've never had a nickname before.

Narrator: But Tate noticed that some people didn't call him anything at all. In fact, some kids didn't even talk to him anymore.

Tate: Rose never hangs around like she used to. And where's Eddie these days? I never see. ... *(notices Brody, Jordan, Rose, and Eddie entering)* Oh, I get it! Brody and Jordan have been working on them. *(to others)* So are you guys too good for me now?

Eddie: We didn't say that!

Rose: We're just tired of your language, Tate.

Eddie: It seemed kind of funny at first, but now you're out of control, man.

Tate: Oh, come on!

Jordan: He's right. It's like a habit.

Brody: Yeah. You don't even know you're doing it sometimes.

Tate: Of course I do! And I can stop any time.

Jordan: I don't think so, Tate.

Tate: Oh, what the *flooglemump* do you know?

Narrator: See? See? Um ... that's what you're supposed to say, Eddie.

Eddie: I know! *(to Tate)* See?

Tate: I said that on purpose, OK? Why don't you all just leave me alone, you *flooglemumps!*

Brody: Good idea. *(exits)*

Rose: Yeah! *(exits)*

Eddie: Gladly! *(exits)*

Jordan: How could you call us names? I ... I thought we were friends. *(exits)*

Tate: Friends don't act like they're better than you and criticize every little thing you say. Luckily, I have plenty of other friends. Plenty.

Scene Seven

Narrator: So Tate decided to concentrate on those other friends. Of course, he threw around a lot of bad language, just to keep them entertained. A lot!

Tate: But it's not like Brody and the others said. I can clean up my act any time I want.

Narrator: Sure. You're in control.

Tate: (*acting tough*) Yep! "The Mouth" is in control! Uh-huh. That's right. I'm the master.

Coach Jamison: (*entering and surprising Tate*) Tate, I want to talk to you.

Tate: (*in squeaky, startled voice*) OK!

Coach Jamison: I heard you're still using bad language. And you're using nastier words. And you're using them more often. *And* you're using them against people.

Tate: (*muttering*) It's not really a big deal.

Coach Jamison: I think it is. You know I don't allow cursing in my classes, on the field, or even in the locker room. But do you know why?

Tate: (*annoyed*) No.

Coach Jamison: It's because of Saint Bernardine of Siena. Ever hear of him?

Tate: (*sighs*) No.

Coach Jamison: I was … well, inspired, I guess … when I learned about him. See, he didn't like bad language. Even when he was a kid, he wouldn't allow anyone to swear around him.

Tate: Gee. He sounds fun.

Coach Jamison: Fun enough, I guess. Trying to be a good person didn't keep him from having plenty of friends.

Tate: Oh.

Coach Jamison: And he was pretty popular as an adult, too. He really wanted to preach about God, but his voice was too weak. Back then they didn't have microphones, so that was a real problem. But Bernardine prayed to the Virgin Mary, and his voice became strong and—

Tate: This is like a really cool story, Coach. Really. And I get it, OK? You're saying I can be popular without cursing. I get it. And I'll watch my language from now on.

Coach Jamison: Let me finish. Bernardine became one of the most popular preachers ever. He affected thousands of people. And do you know what his favorite topic was?

Tate: (*sighs*) How to be popular without swearing?

Coach Jamison: No. He preached a lot about the Holy Name of Jesus. He used the Holy Name over and over in his sermons, and he liked to hold up a special symbol of Jesus' name. He inspired lots of people to love and honor the Holy Name of Jesus, too.

Tate: But I honor Jesus' name. I don't take his name in vain. That's not how I talk.

Coach Jamison: But think about the language you do use, Tate. Do you really believe it honors the Lord to say his name with the same mouth that said *those* words?

Tate: I … uh … I …

Coach Jamison: Or to pray to him after you've dirtied that mouth with foul language?

Tate: I … uh … I …

Coach Jamison: Well?

Tate: I guess I never thought of it like that. I … I really get it, Coach. It's not right … the way I've been talking. So I'm going to watch my language from now on.

Coach Jamison: Now where have I heard that before?

Tate: I mean it, Coach. For real this time.

Coach Jamison: That's great. Just great. *(exits)*

Tate: Yeah. I'm cleaning up my language. That'll show those guys they were wrong about me!

Scene Eight

Narrator: But it wasn't so easy for Tate to change the way he talked. When he opened his locker the next morning and everything fell out, he let out a bad word without even thinking.

Tate: *Flooglemump!* Oops! I mean … um … daggone it!

Narrator: *(as Michael and Hunter enter and sit)* And when he saw the disappointing grade on his English test, it happened again.

Tate: Well, *flooglemump!* I mean … Rats! Darn! Dadgummit!

Michael: Hey, Mouth. Mr. Trudeau can't hear you. Go ahead and let loose.

Tate: Um … I … maybe later.

Narrator: And when he squirted ketchup on his shirt at lunch ...

Tate: *Flooglemump!* Aaaugh! I can't believe I said that!

Hunter: Yeah, dude. That was pretty tame for you. Are you sick or something?

Tate: No. I'm just ... I mean ... Do I look *flooglemump* sick?

Michael, Hunter: *(laugh)*

Narrator: Tate just couldn't control his swearing. And if he could, wouldn't his reputation be ruined? He wanted to do the right thing, but what if his new friends dropped him? Didn't he have an obligation to his fans, so to speak? He was really facing quite a—

Tate: OK! OK! There is such a thing as too much narration, you know.

Narrator: Whatever.

Tate: I guess my friends were right. The swearing *is* a habit with me. I don't know if I can stop. And do I even want to? I mean ... Well ... *(gesturing at Narrator)* That stuff he/she said. Maybe Saint Bernardine's friends didn't care about his attitude on bad language, but I think mine will.

Narrator: But ... Never mind.

Tate: And if I lose the friends I still have ... well ... then I won't have any friends at all.

Narrator: But real friends ... Never mind.

Tate: I just don't know what to do.

Narrator: Look ... I mean ... *(sighs)* On with the play.

Scene Nine

Narrator: So things got even more complicated for Tate. He tried to use clean language most of the time. But when he was around his new friends, he had to swear enough to keep them interested. But that made it harder to use appropriate language the rest of the time. *(as Michael and Hunter enter)* Yet he ... Well, we don't want too much narration, do we? So let's proceed.

Tate: My books hit the floor, and he starts to walk away. So I tell him—

Michael: Dude! You've told us this story before.

Hunter: Yeah. Hey, do you know any ... you know ... jokes?

Tate: Jokes? Well … um … Knock-knock!

Michael and Hunter: Who's there?

Tate: Orange.

Michael and Hunter: Orange who?

Tate: Orange you going to open the door? *(laughs)*

Michael: What kind of joke is that?

Hunter: That wasn't dirty at all.

Tate: I … um … don't know any of *that* kind of joke.

Michael: You don't? But you're "The Mouth."

Hunter: You don't know *any* good jokes?

Tate: *Flooglemump* no! *(laughs, but laughter dies as others don't join in)*

Hunter: You're getting kind of boring, man.

Michael: Yeah.

Tate: Did I ever tell you–

Hunter: *(to Michael)* Let's go talk to Ferdinand. I hear he can play "The Star-Spangled Banner" with his armpit.

Michael: Freaky! *(exiting with Hunter)* Hey! Let's call Ferdinand "The Pit."

Tate: But … but … *(to Narrator)* Now I don't have any friends left! What am I going to do?

Narrator: *(says nothing)*

Tate: Why don't you say something?

Narrator: Me? Oh, I'm just the narrator. Nobody wants to hear my comments.

Tate: Um … right. Man! I want to do the right thing … I want to use clean language and honor God like Saint Bernardine … I really do. And I want to have friends, too. My life is so messed up!

Narrator: What a shame.

Tate: Can't you help me out here? I'm all alone now! Completely friendless!

Narrator: My. Isn't that … Oh, OK! Are you sure about that friendless thing? It seems to me you had some pretty good friends before.

Tate: Yeah. *Real* friends. Too bad I ruined everything with them. I wish I knew how to fix that.

Narrator: Come on, Tate. You know what to do. Don't you?

Tate: Yeah. I guess so. I just hope it works!

Scene Ten

Narrator: *(as Jordan, Brody, Rose, and Eddie enter)* It wasn't easy for Tate to talk to his old friends.

Brody: Look! It's "The Mouth"!

Rose: Everybody, cover your ears.

Tate: Listen ...

Jordan: We're afraid to!

Tate: I don't blame you, but please ... let me apologize.

Eddie: Can you do that without swearing?

Tate: Yes! Look, you guys were right about my language. I was really out of control, but I didn't want to admit that so I ... attacked you. I'm sorry. I ... I hope you can forgive me.

Brody: I think we can do that.

Eddie: Yeah. Since you apologized.

Rose: But you really have a problem, Tate.

Tate: I know! And I'm working on it.

Jordan: Hey, maybe we can help you.

Tate: That would be great. But how?

Jordan: Well, maybe we could do something when you swear. Like pinch you real hard.

Others: Yeah! Good idea! *Etc.*

Tate: I don't know ...

Brody: *(laughs)* We're just joking.

Jordan: But I do have a real idea. You know that noise they make when somebody gives the wrong answer on a game show. It's like *hooooooonk!* We could do that when you mess up.

Tate: OK. Thanks.

Brody: Hey, let's practice.

Narrator: *(in spurts, trying to speak between Tate's friends honking and laughing)* So, with the help of his friends, Tate cleaned up his act. Sure, he still slips up once in a while, but when he ... Excuse me! Trying to narrate here!

Others: *(exit muttering)*

Narrator: So anyway ... when Tate backslides, he thinks of Saint Bernardine, says a prayer, and focuses on the Holy Name of Jesus. That has really helped him get control of his mouth. *(loud burst of honking and laughing)* Now if he could just get control of his friends!

SAINT BERNARDINE
OF SIENNA

Friends in the Hand

SUMMARY

How can Alyssa make friends at camp when she's being judged by the company she keeps? Between dweeby Nolan and religious Beth, Alyssa will never fit in!

COSTUMES/SETS/PROPS

All characters wear clothing appropriate to camp. Nolan could dress strangely.
Tables and chairs can serve as the mess hall. Another area with benches or cots could serve as the girls' cabin.
If props are desired, the following can be used: bags and packs, a stuffed rabbit, a family photo, two rosaries, cafeteria trays, a fake campfire, and playing cards.

PRESENTATION

Alyssa gets annoyed with herself whenever she uses an old saying.
In Scenes Two, Five, and Nine, all campers can appear and mime appropriate actions, or the scenes can be performed with just the main characters. Beth mimes praying in Scene Five. In Scene Six, Alyssa, Beth, and Nolan mime moving around.

Cast

Narrator

Alyssa

Beth

Nolan

Mariel and Travis, counselors

Girl campers: Jen, Kiri

Boy campers: Chico, Ronnie

About Saint Paul

Saul, a devout Jew of the first century, persecuted early Christians until Jesus appeared to him on the road to Damascus. With this encounter, Saul converted to Christianity and devoted himself to spreading the faith. Using his Roman name, Paul, he traveled extensively, speaking about Jesus everywhere. He also wrote inspiring letters, or "epistles," which are included in the New Testament. Despite hardships, physical abuse, and imprisonments, Paul never stopped trying to bring others to Jesus. It's believed he was beheaded in Rome around the year 67, during Nero's persecution of the Christians. Saint Paul's feast day, shared with Saint Peter, is June 29. His conversion is celebrated on January 25. Saint Paul is the patron of converts and journalists.

Friends in the Hand

Scene One

Narrator: At first Alyssa was glad her friend Beth was going to the same camp she was.

Alyssa: At least we'll know *somebody* there.

Beth: Yeah, but we'll get to know other people. And make lots of new friends.

Alyssa: That's what my parents say. They think camp is the best thing since sliced bread.

Beth: Is that one of those old sayings they're always … um … saying?

Alyssa: *(sighs)* Ye-es. I'm so used to hearing that stuff now I'm starting to sound just like them. I guess the apple doesn't fall far from the tree. Aaugh! That's another one!

Beth: Maybe it's good you're getting a little vacation from them.

Alyssa: Yeah. Out of sight out of … Aaugh! I have to stop doing that!

Beth: Relax. Soon we'll be getting away from it all at Camp Lonely Bear.

Alyssa: Right. I'm so happy you're going, too. I'd hate for my first time at camp to be like Camp Lonely Alyssa Who Nobody Talks To.

Beth: Don't worry. Hey, all's well when you … um … stitch … in time.

Alyssa: You'd better leave the old sayings to the professionals.

Scene Two

Narrator: Alyssa was really nervous about camp—as nervous as a long-tailed cat in a room full of rocking chairs. *(to Alyssa)* Ever hear that one?

Alyssa: *(dully)* Yes. I've heard them all.

Narrator: Oh. Well, once they got to camp, Alyssa felt even more nervous.

Alyssa: Look at these people! Wow! They seem so much cooler than we do.

Beth: Excuse me?

Alyssa: Sorry. I'm just worried about meeting people, I guess.

Beth: *(as Nolan enters)* There's somebody we don't have to meet.

Alyssa: *(making a face)* Nolan! What's he doing here?

Nolan: Hi, you guys!

Alyssa and Beth: *(singsong)* Hi, Nolan.

Alyssa: We didn't know you were coming to this camp. Man! It's a small world. *(to self)* Rats!

Nolan: *(laughing obnoxiously)* I know what you mean, but the earth's circumference is 24,901.55 miles at the equator, so one could not properly call it "small."

Alyssa: Uh-huh. Hey, don't you need to register?

Nolan: Yes, I do. See you later! *(exits)*

Alyssa: I hope not!

Beth: But he's nice.

Alyssa: No one here knows that. He's going to seem like a complete dweeb to everybody.

Beth: Well, they shouldn't judge a book by its ... um ... table of contents?

Alyssa: By its cover. And you're right—but people do it anyway. That's why I don't want to be around Nolan. I hate to say it ... really! ... but you *are* judged by the company you keep.

Beth: I guess.

Scene Three

Narrator: Soon the girls met their counselor.

Mariel: *(entering)* Hi! I'm Mariel.

Alyssa and Beth: *(singsong)* Hi, Mariel.

Narrator: *(as Jen and Kiri enter)* Then they met the other girls in their cabin.

Everyone: (*introducing themselves*)

Mariel: Everybody get unpacked and meet at the mess hall in fifteen minutes. (*exits*)

Jen: Don't laugh, you guys, but I brought Mr. Hoppy. He's this stuffed rabbit I've had forever.

Alyssa: Aaaw! He's as cute as a speckled pup! I mean ... he's really cute.

Kiri: I brought a picture of my family. Did you bring anything from home, Alyssa?

Alyssa: No. Nothing important.

Beth: But didn't you bring—

Alyssa: I brought shampoo and soap, of course. Cleanliness is next to godliness! (*to self*) Darn! Hey, shouldn't we head to the mess hall?

Jen: (*exiting with Kiri*) Yeah. We'd better go.

Beth: So did you bring your rosary?

Alyssa: No. I forgot, OK?

Beth: Well, I brought mine. I'm hanging it on my bedpost. You can borrow it anytime.

Alyssa: You know, the other girls didn't bring anything like that.

Beth: They can borrow it, too.

Alyssa: I didn't mean ... Let's go eat.

Scene Four

Narrator: (*as Travis, Mariel, Jen, and Kiri enter*) While waiting for the mess hall to open, the girls met one of the boys' counselors.

Mariel: Hey, everybody. This is Travis. He's the counselor for our brother cabin.

Girls: (*singsong*) Hi, Travis.

Travis: (*as boys, except Nolan, enter*) And here are the guys in my cabin.

Everyone: (*introducing themselves*)

Nolan: (*enters*) Sorry I'm late! (*to Alyssa and Beth*) I'm in your brother cabin. Isn't that neat-o?

Jen: Neat? O? Did you escape from the 1950s?

Nolan: *(laughing obnoxiously)* Good one! But the slang term "neat-o" was actually popular in the '70s. In the '50s, someone would likely have said "hep" or even "like crazy."

Jen: That's ... interesting.

Kiri: *(to Alyssa)* So, is he your boyfriend?

Alyssa: No! He just goes to my school. That's all.

Nolan: Yeah, we go ... Ooh! The door's opening! Time to eat! *(exits with counselors and boys)*

Jen: I guess he's hungry.

Alyssa: Yeah. Hungry to be normal. What a dork! Hey ... um ... maybe we can get seats together.

Jen: Maybe not. *(exits with Kiri)*

Alyssa: See? Nolan is making us look like dweebs, and nobody wants to be friends with us!

Beth: Maybe Jen just meant it'll be hard to find seats. You shouldn't go leaping without looking.

Alyssa: OK. That's not how the saying goes. And you're wrong about Jen.

Beth: Can't you give things a chance before you decide we're doomed?

Alyssa: *(muttering)* There are none so blind ...

Beth: What?

Alyssa: OK, OK! I'll try.

Scene Five

Narrator: After Alyssa and Beth got their food, there weren't any empty chairs by Jen and Kiri.

Alyssa: *(to Beth)* They could have saved a couple of seats. They just don't like us.

Beth: They never said that.

Alyssa: Actions speak louder than words. Errrrrrr! Must. Stop. Must. Stop.

Narrator: They sat down at the end of the table, and Beth made the sign of the cross and bowed her head. Like they weren't already having trouble fitting in!

Alyssa: Beth! Nobody else is saying grace. You're going to make everybody notice us.

Beth: *I* am? But aren't *you* going to say grace?

Alyssa: I'll … um … just say it in my head … you know … without movements.

Beth: OK.

Narrator: Then Beth bowed her head again. Alyssa knew her friend was praying, but she couldn't tell if anybody else noticed. She hoped not!

Alyssa: *(to self)* I'll never make friends here if Nolan and Beth keep acting like weirdoes!

Scene Six

Narrator: *(as everyone sits around "fire")* After supper, the counselors built a big campfire.

Mariel: Gather around, everybody! It's time for some good old-fashioned camp songs!

Narrator: Alyssa didn't join the fun because she was as worried as a snail in a marching band.

Alyssa: Oh, you just made that up.

Narrator: So? *(to audience)* Anyway … Alyssa was worried because Nolan insisted on hanging around, acting like a complete dweeb and making her look like one, too.

Nolan: Isn't fire amazing? One could argue that mastering fire is man's greatest achievement.

Alyssa: Right. *(to Beth)* And speaking of fire, that smoke's getting in my eyes. Let's move.

Beth: OK.

Narrator: But Nolan followed the girls and sat beside them.

Nolan: Once people could control fire, their whole lives changed. Fire enabled them to—

Alyssa: *(to Beth)* Uh-oh! The wind changed direction. Let's move back.

Narrator: And Nolan came right along. Alyssa made several more excuses to move, but Nolan stuck to the girls like spots on a tiger. *(to Alyssa)* There's a good one.

Alyssa: Sheesh! Tigers don't have spots. *(to Beth)* Nolan's making us look stupid again.

Beth: What do you mean?

Chico: Do you have ants in your pants? *(laughs)*

Ronnie: *(laughing)* Good one!

Alyssa: *(to Beth)* That's what I mean. Let's move again while he's talking to somebody else and see if we can get rid of him for good.

Beth: I don't … oh, all right.

Narrator: But Nolan noticed the girls had moved and hurried right over.

Nolan: *(laughing obnoxiously)* You almost lost me there!

Alyssa: Sheesh! Can't you take a hint, Nolan? We don't want you hanging around us!

Nolan: Oh. OK. Sorry. *(exits)*

Beth: That was mean, Alyssa!

Alyssa: Well, how else were we going to get away from him?

Jen: Hey, your friend looked upset.

Alyssa: He's not my friend, OK? Everybody knows that birds of a feather … I mean … I'm nothing like him. Like I would be friends with a loser like that!

Kiri: Whatever.

Scene Seven

Narrator: *(as counselors and boys exit)* As the girls got ready for bed that night, Jen and Kiri didn't seem very friendly. Obviously Alyssa *was* being judged by the company she kept! Nolan's dorkiness was rubbing off on her. And being friends with Beth made her look religious.

Alyssa: *(to self)* Not that there's anything wrong with religion. But does she have to be so obvious? I hope she doesn't start praying right here. I'd better keep the other girls busy with something. *(to others)* Does anybody want to play cards? I have some here in my pack.

Narrator: Unfortunately, as she yanked the cards out, she accidentally pulled out her rosary, too.

Beth: You found it!

Alyssa: Why did you put this in my bag, Beth? Instead of yours? I guess you got confused, huh?

Beth: Yeah. I'm confused all right. Why would I bring two—

Alyssa: So here you go. Take it.

Beth: Um … OK.

Mariel: *(entering)* Lights out, girls! Good night! *(exits)*

Alyssa: Good night, everybody! Sleep tight! And don't let—

Jen: Good night, Alyssa!

Alyssa: Yeah. Good night.

Scene Eight

Narrator: *(as Jen and Kiri exit)* Alyssa tossed and turned for hours that night.

Alyssa: Nolan and Beth are ruining camp for me! What am I going to do?

Narrator: Luckily, the campfire incident had crushed Nolan like a bug under a steamroller.

Alyssa: Please!

Narrator: *(as counselors and campers enter)* So he didn't even try to talk to the girls at the flagpole the next morning.

Beth: Nolan is avoiding us. I think you hurt his feelings last night.

Alyssa: I'm sorry, but I had to do it.

Travis: Listen up, everybody! We have a busy schedule here, but you will get one free period daily. During that time, you can take special lessons like archery, basket-weaving, and other fun stuff. Please sign up for the lessons on the bulletin board in the mess hall.

Mariel: And if you want to take the shuttle to Sunday Mass, you can sign up for that, too.

Narrator: After saying the pledge to the flag, everybody headed to breakfast.

Beth: *(as everyone except Alyssa and Nolan exit)* Hey, Nolan.

Nolan: Hello … Beth.

Beth: Want to sit with us?

Nolan: No thank you. *(exits)*

Beth: See? He *is* upset about what you said!

Alyssa: He's OK. Sticks and stones break the bones, but words … Oh, for Pete's sake! Darn! Darn! Darn! Let's eat already.

Scene Nine

Narrator: When the girls got inside, there were a lot of people at the bulletin board.

Alyssa: Maybe we'd better sign up for stuff before we eat.

Beth: Good idea. But what should we take?

Alyssa: So many things sound like fun.

Beth: Well, I know one thing I want to do for sure.

Narrator: Beth went and signed up for the shuttle to Mass. Alyssa couldn't believe it!

Ronnie: *(entering with Chico)* Look! Beth's going to church!

Chico: Isn't that sweet? *(exits, laughing, with Ronnie)*

Beth: What's their problem?

Alyssa: I hate to say anything, but honesty *is* the best policy. Errrr! Anyway … you're not coming off too well, Beth.

Beth: I'm not?

Alyssa: No. You look like … well … a religious nut. We'll never fit in as long as you act like that.

Beth: "We"?

Alyssa: You just need to tone it down a little, OK? Like maybe pack away your rosaries.

Beth: One of those is yours!

Alyssa: Shhh! And why don't you take your name off the Mass list? Nobody else has signed up.

Beth: But aren't you going to Mass?

Narrator: Obviously, Beth still didn't understand the situation! But before Alyssa could explain further, Jen and Kiri came along.

Jen: *(entering with Kiri)* So what lessons are you taking, Beth?

Alyssa: We don't know yet. How about you?

Kiri: We haven't decided. It looks like a lot of the lists are full already. Hey! There's a list with only one person signed up.

Beth: That's me. It's the list for the shuttle to Mass.

Jen: You're going to church even though you're at camp?

Kiri: That's amazing.

Alyssa: *(snorts)* No kidding! I mean … this is camp! A place to get away from everything! What kind of dope wants to go to church while they're here?

Beth: Gee, thanks, Alyssa. *(exits)*

Jen: *(to Kiri)* Talk about lame!

Alyssa: I know! I've tried talking to her, but it doesn't do any good.

Kiri: *(to Jen)* Some people just don't get it.

Jen: Yeah. *(exits with Kiri)*

Alyssa: *(calling after them)* Hey, wait up, you guys!

Scene Ten

Narrator: Alyssa figured she'd eat breakfast with Jen and Kiri, but Nolan came along and stopped her before she could get into the food line.

Nolan: Could we talk?

Alyssa: Look, I'm sorry about last night, but it's a dog-eat-dog world … I mean … it's tough here …

Nolan: I get it, OK? I'm a big nerd, and you don't want to be seen with me.

Alyssa: Yeah … well … I'm glad you understand.

Nolan: But I wanted to talk about Beth, not me. I heard that stuff you said to her—about not acting religious. And I saw how you made fun of her. Why would you hurt her feelings like that?

Alyssa: Because she's just as bad as you are. I mean … you make me look … you know …

Nolan: Like a dweeb?

Alyssa: Yeah. Sorry.

Nolan: And Beth makes you look ... ?

Alyssa: You know ... religious ... holy ... saintly ... that kind of thing.

Nolan: So you're afraid Beth will make you look *(gasps)* Christian?

Alyssa: Yes, exactly. Wait. No, not exactly. Well, the way you say it doesn't sound right!

Nolan: *(sadly)* No, it doesn't.

Alyssa: *(muttering)* I'm just trying to fit in.

Nolan: Look, Alyssa. You don't have to stand up in the mess hall and start preaching—

Alyssa: Really? Thanks for clearing that up, Nolan.

Nolan: What I mean is: You don't have to act all holy, but it's not right to *hide* your Christianity. Think of everything Saint Paul went through for his faith. Like he traveled around for years, preaching about Jesus, and he—

Alyssa: OK, this is what I'm talking about. The whole human encyclopedia thing is so dorky.

Nolan: Just listen! Sometimes Saint Paul didn't even have enough to eat or drink. He was whipped, beaten up, arrested, and thrown into prison. But nothing stopped him from talking and writing about Jesus. Nothing but death.

Alyssa: This is just camp, OK? If I keep a few things private here, what's the big deal?

Nolan: Wow. You really don't get it. *(exits as Jen and Kiri enter)*

Scene Eleven

Narrator: Finally, Alyssa got her tray—and a seat beside Jen and Kiri.

Alyssa: Hi, you guys!

Jen: Look, Alyssa. I'm really, really sorry, but we don't want to be friends with you.

Alyssa: But ... but why not?

Kiri: It's just ... well ... you're judged by the company you keep.

Alyssa: That stupid Nolan! He's making me look like a dork, isn't he?

Jen: Right. Because talking like my great-granny is so cool.

Alyssa: *(muttering)* I'm working on that.

Jen: This isn't about Nolan anyway.

Alyssa: It's Beth, isn't it? Listen, we get along, but we're not really that much alike.

Kiri: No kidding! *She's* nice.

Jen: Yeah! I guess she takes being a Christian seriously. I mean … she really lives it.

Kiri: So, anyway … we have to consider our reputations and hang around with nice, kind people.

Alyssa: Hey, I'm nice! And kind! And I'm a Christian, too.

Kiri: Really?

Jen: It's kind of hard to tell. *(exits with Kiri)*

Scene Twelve

Narrator: After everyone else left the mess hall, Alyssa sat there, trying to think.

Alyssa: I ditched Nolan. Then Beth. And now I'm getting ditched. I guess what goes around comes around. Aaugh!

Narrator: But Alyssa knew the old sayings weren't her real problem.

Alyssa: I didn't just hide my faith—I ditched it, too! The way I treated those guys wasn't Christian at all. And why did I act like that? Because I was afraid somebody might not like me? Saint Paul sacrificed everything for his faith! But I wasn't willing to sacrifice anything for mine.

Narrator: Alyssa felt lower than a worm in a hole at the bottom of the Grand Canyon.

Alyssa: Good one.

Narrator: You think so? Because I made it up and … um … So Alyssa felt terrible.

Alyssa: I wish I had Saint Paul's strength. Then maybe I could fix things. But I've made my bed and I have to lie in it. Darn! I've burned my bridges and … Rats! An apple a day … Aaaaaaugh!

Narrator: Alyssa felt pretty hopeless, but then she remembered some helpful words.

Alyssa: Every cloud has a silver lining. Yeah. And where there's a will, there's a way. Oh! The journey of a thousand miles begins with a single step. Maybe I shouldn't give up. Saint Paul never did! Maybe I *can* do something.

Narrator: You'll never know until you try.

Alyssa: Yeah.

Scene Thirteen

Narrator: Actually, Alyssa had to try, try again. Nolan and Beth didn't accept her apologies at first. She had to keep showing them she was a true friend. But by the end of camp, her kindness had healed their friendship. Some of the other kids even warmed up to her.

Jen: *(entering with Kiri)* See you next year, Alyssa!

Kiri: E-mail me, OK?

Alyssa: *(as they exit)* OK! Bye!

Narrator: Best of all, Alyssa decided to be more like Saint Paul.

Alyssa: No preaching! But I'm not hiding my faith anymore. I'm going to try to really live it!

Nolan: *(entering with Beth)* This has been great, but I'm ready to go home.

Alyssa: Camp sure was a good experience.

Beth: Was it the best thing since sliced bread?

Alyssa: Yeah, thanks to you guys. You really helped me.

Beth: You know what they say: friends in the hand are worth … a thousand words … times nine?

Nolan: *(laughing obnoxiously)* That's not what they say!

Alyssa: But they should. They really should.

SAINT PAUL

The Chameleon Effect

SUMMARY

Dalton becomes a human chameleon, abandoning his principles to fit into his new neighborhood. Can learning about Blessed Kateri Tekakwitha help him get back on track?

COSTUMES/SETS/PROPS

All characters wear contemporary clothing. Amelia could wear a basketball jersey.

One chair would provide adequate seating.

The following props can be used: basketball, encyclopedia, a stamp album, two baseball gloves and a baseball, books about saints, a football, and a purse with money.

PRESENTATION

When "human chameleon" is mentioned, the speaker pauses to hum or sing dramatic music before saying the phrase. The Audience Member also does this on his/her last line.

Local team names could be substituted in Scene Two.

CAST

Narrator

Audience Member (planted in real audience)

Dalton

Sarah

Amelia

Paco

Dan and Ann, brother and sister

Omar and Erick, Dalton's new friends

Jubilee

ABOUT BLESSED KATERI TEKAKWITHA

Tekakwitha was born in New York in 1656, the daughter of a Mohawk chief and an Algonquin woman. Her mother was Christian, and she taught Tekakwitha about Jesus. When a smallpox epidemic killed Tekakwitha's family, she went to live with relatives. Her relatives and their fellow villagers mistreated her because she was Christian, but Tekakwitha did not abandon her faith. A missionary baptized her when she was twenty, and she took the name "Kateri," Mohawk for "Catherine." About a year later, she walked 200 miles to reach a Christian settlement. Always in poor health, she died after only a few joyful years of living her faith without persecution. In 1980, she became the first Native American to be beatified. Her feast day is celebrated on July 14 in the United States and on April 17 in Canada. She is the patron of Native Americans and the environment.

The Chameleon Effect

Scene One

Narrator: Welcome to an informative presentation on a fascinating topic: "The Chameleon Effect." You all know animals respond to their environments. The puffer fish inflates its body to confuse predators. The arctic fox grows white fur for camouflage during snowy months. And, of course, you've heard of the chameleon, which changes color in response to temperature, light, or danger. But today (tonight) you'll learn about the amazing ... human chameleon!

Audience Member: Ooooh!

Narrator: Let's take a look at a real-life ... human chameleon!

Audience Member: *(as Dalton enters)* He looks like a regular kid.

Narrator: Dalton *was* a regular kid until his environment changed. He moved into a new neighborhood where he didn't know anybody. Having no friends worried him. He actually felt desperate about meeting people and fitting in. So desperate he became ... a human chameleon!

Audience Member: OK, OK, let's get on with it already!

Narrator: Very well. It all started with Sarah ...

Sarah: *(entering)* Hi! I'm Sarah. I live next door.

Dalton: Hi. I'm Dalton.

Sarah: I was thinking I could introduce you to the kids around here.

Dalton: Thanks! That'd be great. So ... um ... how should I act? I mean ... when I meet people?

Sarah: Just act like you, I guess. See you tomorrow! *(exits)*

Narrator: Dalton breathed a big sigh of relief. *(pauses)* I said, "Dalton breathed a big sigh."

Dalton: Oh. *(exaggerated sigh)*

Narrator: *(smug)* But that was a mistake because his problems weren't over.

Dalton: Rats.

Scene Two

Narrator: *(as Sarah and Amelia enter)* The next day, Sarah took Dalton for a walk down their street and introduced him to Amelia, who was shooting baskets.

Amelia: Hi, Dalton. So, do you like basketball?

Narrator: Dalton wasn't into basketball much, but he sensed Amelia was. Afraid to ruin his chance to make a new friend, he became … a human chameleon.

Audience Member: Oooh! He's going to change now.

Dalton: Oh, I'm a big, big basketball fan. Big.

Amelia: Are you a Bulls fan like me?

Dalton: You bet!

Sarah: Personally, I like the Pacers.

Dalton: They're good, too.

Sarah: Well, I'm introducing Dalton to everybody, so we'd better move along.

Amelia: See you around!

Sarah: *(as Amelia exits)* You just made a friend for life since you like Chicago.

Dalton: Yeah. Those Pacers are fantastic.

Sarah: But Chicago's team is the Bulls.

Dalton: I meant to say that.

Audience Member: Sheesh! Human chameleon! He doesn't look any different.

Scene Three

Narrator: *(as Paco enters)* Next, they saw a boy sitting on his porch with a stack of books.

Sarah: Hi, Paco! This is Dalton, my new neighbor.

Dalton: Hi. What are you reading?

Paco: The encyclopedia. I'm up to Volume G.

Narrator: Paco seemed smart, and Dalton wanted to impress him. So, once again, he transformed himself.

Audience Member: This had better be good.

Dalton: I do the same thing, Paco, but I use the dictionary.

Paco: Hey, I think I'll try that.

Sarah: Well, we'll see you later, Paco.

Paco: See you!

Sarah: *(as Paco exits)* I'll bet you can define almost any word, huh?

Dalton: Um … I mean … *(snorts)* What do you think?

Sarah: Right. Of course, you can!

Audience Member: This is a big rip-off. That kid looks just like he did when we came in. He *says* he's different, but … Wait. I get it. He's camouflaging himself, isn't he? First, as a basketball fan. Then as a brainiac. Hey, this could be interesting!

Scene Four

Narrator: Dalton repeatedly displayed the chameleon response. When he met Brad in his workshop, he lied about building a tree house. Later he told Jubilee he shared her passion for *(snickers)* scrapbooking. After that, Sarah introduced him to Dan and Ann.

Dan: *(entering with Ann)* It's great to meet another stamp collector.

Ann: What kind of stamps do you collect, Dalton?

Dalton: The kind that … um … go on letters.

Dan: *(to Ann)* See? *He* doesn't waste his time on cinderellas! *(to Dalton)* Do you?

Dalton: Well … um … *(to Sarah)* Maybe we'd better move along.

Sarah: I guess. Bye, you guys. *(as Dan and Ann exit)* So what are cinderellas?

Dalton: That's hard to explain.

Sarah: My grandfather's a collector, too. He told me cinderellas are stamps that aren't used for postage. Like Easter seals. That's not really a difficult concept.

Dalton: Well, I'm just not good with words.

Sarah: Not good with words! You said you read the dictionary all the time.

Dalton: But that's different! The words aren't … um … in sentences.

Sarah: Look, you don't have to pretend to be somebody you're not to make friends around here.

Dalton: I'm not pretending!

Sarah: So you really are a genius basketball fan who scrapbooks and makes stuff out of wood whenever he's not reading the dictionary or collecting stamps?

Dalton: Yes! That's the real me. I like to do different stuff, OK?

Sarah: Oh. Sorry. I just never met anybody so versatile.

Dalton: What does that mean?

Sarah: Are you kidding? Oh! I guess you are. Ha! Good one.

Dalton: Thanks. I'm … um … kind of a comedian, too.

Audience Member: Boy. He really *is* … a human chameleon.

Narrator: Hey. I'm supposed to say that.

Audience Member: Whatever.

Scene Five

Narrator: *(as Sarah exits)* After that, Sarah had to go home, and Dalton, *(looking at Audience Member)* … the human chameleon, walked to the park, feeling terrible.

Dalton: Why did I act like that? Pretty soon everybody around here will realize I'm a big fake. Man! I blew my chance to make any friends.

Narrator: *(as Omar and Erick enter)* Luckily, he passed two guys playing catch in the park. Their ball came toward him, and he had to throw it back.

Omar: Thanks. Are you the new kid?

Dalton: Yeah. I'm Dalton.

Omar: I'm Omar. This is Erick.

Erick: Want to play?

Narrator: Dalton started to put on an act, like he had with the other kids.

Dalton: Sure! I'm really into baseball. I used to …

Audience Member: There he goes again!

Narrator: But then Dalton realized these guys were his last chance. If he messed up with them, he wouldn't have any friends at all.

Dalton: I mean … I haven't played that much, but I'll give it a try.

Erick: We don't have an extra glove.

Dalton: That's OK.

Omar: Then let's play!

Narrator: So Dalton made two friends while being himself. He was a good, honest person really—not a chameleon! And he decided to keep it real from then on. *(pauses, then clears throat)*

Dalton: Oh. *(stilted)* I'm keeping it real from now on.

Narrator: Oh, sure.

Scene Six

Narrator: Omar and Erick asked Dalton to meet them at the park the next afternoon. On his way there, Dalton ran into Sarah.

Sarah: *(entering)* Hi. Where are you off to?

Dalton: The park. I'm meeting Omar and Erick. Do you know them?

Sarah: *(frowning)* Yes. I hate to talk about anybody, but those guys get into trouble a lot. Why don't you try to be friends with the kids I introduced to you?

Dalton: Look, Sarah. I can pick my own friends, OK?

Sarah: OK. Sure. Well, see you later. *(exits)*

Narrator: *(as Omar and Erick enter)* When Dalton got to the park, Omar and Erick took him on the nature trail. At one point, the trail passed close to some houses, and the guys walked off into somebody's yard, went right up to a house, and peeked in the back door.

Omar: Nice place! Come here and look.

Narrator: Dalton felt uncomfortable nosing around somebody else's property, but he told himself it wouldn't hurt to look.

Dalton: *(stilted)* Yeah. It won't hurt to just look.

Erick: Huh?

Dalton: Nothing. Let me see … This *is* nice! So … how about we finish that hike?

Narrator: But Omar tried to open the door!

Omar: It's locked. Man! I was hoping to put that mini-TV in my bedroom.

Dalton: You mean … you were going to take it?

Erick: *(threatening)* Do you have a problem with that?

Dalton: I … um …

Omar: *(laughing)* Dude, we're just joking. We're not burglars!

Dalton: *(relieved)* Oh, good!

Erick: We don't have to be burglars. People leave all kinds of things just lying around.

Omar: Right. It's so easy to pick up good stuff. Like that football over by the garage.

Erick: Hey, let's take it to the park and play with it. Sound good to you, Dalton?

Narrator: Dalton knew stealing was wrong, but he was afraid to make his new—and only!—friends mad. So, once again, he let the chameleon effect take over.

Dalton: Sure! Sounds great.

Erick: OK, I'll get it.

Narrator: *(as Omar and Erick exit)* While the guys played with the football, Dalton told himself again and again that taking it wasn't a big deal.

Dalton: *(stilted)* Yeah. It's just a football. What's the big deal?

Narrator: But nothing he said could make the situation seem right.

Audience Member: Of course not! It's not like you can camouflage reality.

Scene Seven

Narrator: Over the next few days, Dalton hung out a lot with Omar and Erick. He was there when they took some tennis equipment, a cooler, and a skateboard out of yards near the park. Each time, he wanted to refuse to go along, but he kept acting like a … human chameleon. He felt bad about that, but he told himself he had no choice.

Dalton: *(stilted)* I have no choice. *(normal)* Not if I want to have some friends!

Narrator: *(as Sarah enters)* One day, Dalton saw Sarah out on her porch with a stack of books.

Dalton: *(joking)* Are you trying to imitate Paco?

Sarah: *(laughing)* Not exactly. I'm studying the saints for my religion class. Right now, I'm reading about Blessed Kateri Tekakwitha, the first Native American to be declared Blessed. She learned about Christianity from her mother. Then her family died of a terrible disease, and she had to live with relatives who hated Christians. She could have given up on her faith, but she knew that wasn't right and she stuck to it.

Dalton: *(sighs)* Sometimes it can be hard to do what's right.

Sarah: It was really hard for her! Her mean relatives didn't give her any food on Sundays because she wouldn't work on God's holy day. People in her village threw rocks at her and threatened death if she didn't give up Christianity. But she refused to do it.

Dalton: Great story. Well, I'd better get going …

Sarah: Wait! She walked two hundred miles through wilderness to reach a Christian settlement. When she got there, she finally received Holy Communion and—

Dalton: Sorry, Sarah, but I have to meet Omar and Erick.

Sarah: You know, stuff keeps disappearing around here, and people suspect those guys. Why are you friends with them? You seem like a good person. Don't you want to do what's right?

Dalton: You told me that story just to lay a guilt trip on me, didn't you?

Sarah: I didn't know you were going to walk by! But maybe you *should* think about Blessed Kateri Tekakwitha. *She* had some principles!

Dalton: Principles?

Sarah: I guess you haven't gotten to the Ps in your dictionary. Principles are morals ... you know ... doing the right thing. A person with principles sticks to them no matter how tough things get. Does that definition fit you, Dalton? *(exits)*

Dalton: *(mad)* What dream world does she live in? Principles are great—and I believe in doing the right thing. But this is real life! You can't do just good stuff! That's unrealistic!

Scene Eight

Narrator: Dalton didn't care what Sarah thought. He wasn't making any changes in—

Audience Member: Man! That kid is such a chameleon, he doesn't even know that he *is* changing! He's changing into this person who ... I mean ... Sorry.

Narrator: The next time Dalton met up with Omar and Erick, things got really out of hand. The guys found a purse left on a porch, and Omar opened it up and took out some money.

Dalton: *(timidly)* What are you doing?

Omar: Don't worry. You'll get your cut.

Dalton: Oh. OK. I mean ... I'd better.

Erick: I hear somebody in the house. Run!

Narrator: *(as Omar and Erick exit)* The guys took off in different directions. Dalton collapsed on a bench down the street. He felt awful because he knew he had to admit the truth now.

Dalton: Do I really have to?

Narrator: Yes!

Dalton: *(stilted)* I have to admit the truth. *(upset)* Sarah was right. I *don't* have any principles! I thought I was a good person, but I'm just a wimp who's too chicken to do the right thing!

Narrator: Dalton told himself—

Dalton: Stop telling me what to say! I can talk to myself about what a loser I am without your help.

Scene Nine

Narrator: So Dalton just sat there ... um ... talking to himself ... until the last person on earth he wanted to see came along.

Sarah: *(entering)* Hey, what's wrong?

Dalton: Me! I'm wrong! Completely, totally wrong!

Sarah: Does this have anything to do with Omar and Erick?

Dalton: Yes. They *are* stealing stuff. *(softly)* And I've been going along with it.

Sarah: You know that's not right.

Dalton: I know! And if I was like that saint you told me about, I could stick to my principles. But I'm not that strong. I don't even know if I *have* principles.

Sarah: Of course you do! You wouldn't be upset if you didn't. But it's like you said before—it can be hard to do what's right.

Dalton: Yeah. Really hard. And I don't have what it takes to do that.

Sarah: Hey, maybe thinking about Blessed Kateri Tekakwitha could help you do the right thing.

Dalton: She *is* pretty inspiring.

Sarah: You know, prayer really gave her strength. That might help you, too.

Dalton: *(brightening)* Yeah! I'll bet it would.

Sarah: Oh, and friends could help you, too.

Dalton: *(sadly)* If I had any friends around here. Besides Omar and Erick. Listen, Sarah. I ... I haven't been honest with you. Or the other kids. You guys don't know the real me.

Sarah: Wait. Are you saying you're *not* a genius basketball fan who scrapbooks and makes stuff out of wood whenever he's not reading the dictionary or collecting stamps?

Dalton: That's what I'm saying, all right. I was worried about making friends so I put on a big act and lied to everybody. I'm sorry.

Sarah: Wow. It must have been really hard to admit that.

Dalton: Yeah. It was. Really, really hard.

Sarah: Well, if you're strong enough to do something that hard then you *do* have what it takes to make things right in your life. Don't you? *(exits)*

Audience Member: I don't know ... A leopard can't change its spots. How can a chameleon change his life?

Narrator: Hey, chameleons are all about change. Maybe Dalton can change for the better.

Audience Member: I hope so.

Scene Ten

Narrator: Dalton thought about everything Sarah had said.

Dalton: Maybe she's right about me. Maybe I *can* be like Blessed Kateri Tekakwitha. Maybe I *can* straighten out my life and do the right thing. Maybe I *can*—

Narrator: That's when Dalton saw Omar and Erick headed his way.

Dalton: Maybe not.

Audience Member: See?

Narrator: Dalton was worried, but he told himself he could stick to his principles.

Dalton: *(stilted)* I can stick to my principles. *(confidently)* I mean ... I can stick to my principles!

Omar: *(entering with Erick)* That was close!

Erick: Here's your share of the money, Dalton.

Dalton: I ... I don't want it.

Omar: Why not?

Dalton: Because it's stolen.

Erick: So? You never minded before.

Dalton: But I should have. It's not right to steal, and I'm not going along with it anymore. If I find out you've stolen anything else, I'll have to turn you in. And you should return all that stuff you took, too.

Omar: Come on, Erick. We're wasting our time with this loser. *(exits with Erick)*

Dalton: I did it! I stood up for what's right! I straightened out my life! I stuck to my principles!

Audience Member: Get real.

Dalton: Huh?

Narrator: Dalton thought. *(looks at Dalton)* He thought hard. *(pause)* Long and hard. *(pause)* And finally he realized something still wasn't right in his life.

Dalton: What are you . . . ? Oh. Oh, yeah.

Narrator: *(prompting)* And Dalton told himself . . . ?

Dalton: I still have to get real with the other kids. That's going to be tough. But I have to do it.

Scene Eleven

Narrator: So Dalton went around the neighborhood, admitting the truth and apologizing. Some kids took it pretty well.

Paco: *(entering)* It's OK. We can be friends as long you never again resort to prevarication.

Dalton: I won't! And I'm not going to lie anymore either.

Narrator: *(as Paco exits)* Others didn't react so positively.

Jubilee: *(entering)* I could never be friends with someone who would lie about . . . *(overcome with emotion)* scrapbooking! *(exits)*

Sarah: *(entering)* I heard you've been straightening things out with everybody.

Dalton: Well, I've been trying. I'm afraid things are ruined for good with some people, but at least I'm on the right track now. You know, you can change a lot of things . . . your neighborhood . . . your hobbies . . . your socks . . . But you can't change your principles. I mean . . . then they're not principles anymore! And you're not the person God wants you to be. Blessed Kateri Tekakwitha sure understood that. And now I do, too.

Sarah: That's great, Dalton. Hey, do you want play a game or something?

Dalton: Sure!

Narrator: *(as Dalton and Sarah exit)* So Dalton changed again—this time into the kind of person he really wanted to be. Of course, he would always have to be on the alert for the chameleon effect.

Audience Member: But if he has trouble again, he can get some help from … the friendship effect!

Narrator: *(muttering)* I was going to say that.

BLESSED
KATERI TEKAKWITHA

There's Nobody Like Rachel

SUMMARY

Sometimes Rachel displays a superior attitude that bothers her friends. They try to get her to face the truth about herself, but how do you convince somebody like Rachel she's a snob?

COSTUMES/SETS/PROPS

All characters wear contemporary clothing. Mr. Stewart could wear a uniform.
A few chairs and a shelf can be used for the bookstore and the meeting room.
The following props can be used: a broom or mop for Mr. Stewart, books for the bookstore, two telephones, some dollar bills, and a book about Saint Clare.

PRESENTATION

In Scene One, Rachel's friends act uncomfortable when they talk about her.
In Scene Two, Mr. Stewart could sweep or mop his way onstage.
All blah-ing should have expression as if sentences are being spoken.

CAST

Narrator

Rachel

Caleb, Liz, Brad, and Kellie—Rachel's friends

Mr. Stewart, custodian

Salesclerk

Montana, new girl

Mr. Diaz, youth group sponsor

 ## ABOUT SAINT CLARE

Clare was born into a wealthy family in Italy around 1193. She could have married well, but she followed the teachings of Saint Francis of Assisi instead, abandoning material things to live in poverty as Jesus did. Despite frequent illness, Clare led an order of religious sisters for forty years, guiding them in this special way of life. She was declared a saint just two years after her death. Saint Clare's feast day is August 11. She is the patron of needleworkers and television.

There's Nobody Like Rachel

Scene One

Narrator: Rachel's friends thought she was nice.

Brad: Yeah. Remember how she brought us souvenirs from her vacation?

Kellie: That was nice.

Caleb: She's always helping me study.

Liz: And she listens when I need to talk.

Caleb: Yeah. There's nobody like Rachel.

Kellie: That's true.

Liz: Yep. Nobody like Rachel.

Brad: She's really nice.

Others: Yeah. Mm-hmm. She sure is. *Etc.*

Narrator: But—obviously—there was something about Rachel that bothered her friends.

Caleb: Sometimes she's . . . I don't know . . .

Kellie: I know what you mean.

Liz: She's just so . . .

Rachel: *(entering)* Hi, you guys!

Others: *(nervous)* Hi! Hi, Rachel! *Etc.*

Rachel: What are you talking about?

Brad: Nothing.

Rachel: *(teasing)* Oh, I get it. You were talking about me. I hope it was all good.

Others: *(laughing)* You bet! Of course! *Etc.*

Rachel: Well, all right then! *(exits)*

Others: *(laughing and calling after her)* Bye! See you later! *Etc.*

Narrator: She really does seem nice.

Others: Oh, she is! Uh-huh! She's nice! *Etc.*

Scene Two

Narrator: Yes, Rachel's friends thought she was nice. But there was *something* about her that concerned them. *(to others)* So what *is* the problem?

Caleb: We-ell ... Say we're in school ...

Narrator: OK. You're in school.

Caleb: Funny. So anyway ... sometimes Rachel acts like this at school ...

Rachel: *(entering)* Is everybody ready for the history test?

Caleb: You bet! Thanks for helping me study.

Rachel: No, thank *you*! It was a good review for me.

Narrator: Wow. She *is* horrible. Awful. How do you stand it?

Caleb: Just wait.

Mr. Stewart: *(enters mopping)* Good morning, everybody.

Brad: Good morning, Mr. Stewart.

Kellie: How are you today?

Mr. Stewart: I'm just fine. How are all of you?

Liz: Fine.

Caleb: Great.

Mr. Stewart: Glad to hear it! You all have a nice day. *(exits)*

Others (except Rachel): *(calling after him)* You, too! Bye! *Etc.*

Rachel: So anyway ... the test. I think Mrs. Adams will ask—

Brad: Why didn't you say anything to Mr. Stewart?

Liz: Yeah. You never talk to him.

Rachel: What would somebody like me say to somebody like him? He's a custodian. We have nothing in common.

Caleb: Except that you're both human beings.

Rachel: I'm not putting him down. I just don't know how to talk to him.

Caleb: *(muttering)* But you don't even try.

Scene Three

Narrator: Hmmm … I think I'm beginning to understand.

Brad: Well, you should see how she acts at stores and restaurants.

Rachel: I love this bookstore.

Caleb: I wonder if they have that new mystery book.

Brad: You mean *The Mystery of the Missing Secret Code*? I don't see it.

Rachel: *(as salesclerk enters)* You'd think they'd have people around to help. Oh. There's somebody. Hey! You! Where's that *Mystery of the Missing Secret Code* book?

Salesclerk: It's in the mystery section, displayed at—

Rachel: No kidding. The mystery section! Like I couldn't figure that out myself!

Salesclerk: I was going to say it's displayed at the end of the aisle. I'd be glad to show you.

Rachel: OK. Come on, everybody.

Salesclerk: Here it is.

Others: *(to clerk)* Thanks for your help. Thank you. *Etc.*

Salesclerk: You're welcome. *(exits)*

Liz: Sheesh, Rachel! You could have thanked the clerk.

Rachel: For what? He's (she's) just doing his (her) job. And not that well, really. You'd think a good customer like me would get better service. *(exits)*

Caleb: Brother.

Scene Four

Narrator: Wow. She isn't as nice as I first thought.

Kellie: She's mostly nice. But she gets this attitude like some people aren't good enough for her.

Brad: Yeah. Even other kids! She won't bother to talk to anybody who's not in our group. Like she'll completely ignore other kids who sit at our lunch table.

Liz: She won't even say hi to anybody she passes on the street or in the mall.

Caleb: Rachel really has a problem. We should try to help her.

Brad: I don't know what we can do.

Kellie: Me neither. If we say anything, we might hurt her feelings.

Liz: She's nice except for that one thing. Maybe we should just let it go.

Narrator: But when Montana joined youth group, Rachel's friends couldn't stand by any longer.

Scene Five

Narrator: *(as Rachel and Montana enter)* That night, while everyone was waiting for the sponsor, Mr. Diaz, to arrive, Montana walked up to Rachel and her friends.

Montana: Hi! I'm Montana.

Others (except Rachel): *(introducing themselves)*

Montana: Nice to meet you. I'm new here so—

Rachel: We got that. The meeting's starting soon. Why don't you sit in that empty seat up front?

Montana: Um … OK. *(moves away and sits)*

Caleb: Rachel! You should have asked her to sit with us.

Rachel: But we don't know her. So why would I do that?

Kellie: Gee, I don't know. Maybe because it would be nice.

Rachel: Hey, I was nice! I told her the meeting would start soon. I pointed her toward a seat. She's probably happy just to have somebody to guide her.

Liz: But you shouldn't … It's not … Help me out here, guys.

Brad: You're right, Liz.

Caleb: Totally right.

Kellie: Yep. Right.

Liz: *(sarcastic)* Thanks.

Caleb: OK, Rachel, the problem is you don't treat everybody equally. You're only nice to certain people—the ones you don't think are beneath you.

Rachel: Are you calling me a snob?

Brad: *(muttering)* If the huge personality defect fits …

Rachel: What?

Caleb: You just need to be nicer, OK?

Rachel: I. Am. Nice! Do I have to be best friends with everybody?

Liz: No, but—

Rachel: Good. Because I'm not going to be friends with Wyoming.

Kellie: That's Montana.

Rachel: Whatever.

Scene Six

Narrator: *(as Mr. Diaz enters)* Mr. Diaz arrived right then, and the meeting started.

Mr. Diaz: Welcome, Montana. Could you tell us a little about yourself?

Montana: Well, we just moved here. My dad's company transferred him. This is the third time that's happened. Oh, and we live at The Oaks because of my mom's—

Rachel: The Oaks? Up on the hill? That The Oaks? The really huge The Oaks?

Montana: Yes.

Rachel: Wow. That place is a mansion. It's enormous!

Montana: I know! I keep getting lost.

Rachel: Wow. Well, welcome! Hey, maybe you should sit by me so I can explain things to you.

Montana: Thanks … um … ?

Rachel: I'm Rachel.

Liz: *(to others)* No, she's not. She's some kind of alien in Rachel's body.

Brad: Hey, Caleb. Maybe you actually got through to her.

Caleb: *(suspicious)* Or maybe not.

Scene Seven

Narrator: As the meeting went on, Rachel continued to be surprisingly nice to Montana.

Mr. Diaz: Let's talk about our lock-in.

Rachel: *(to Montana)* That's when we get to stay overnight in the parish center and play games and eat and talk. I hope you can come.

Mr. Diaz: So who can bring some snacks to the lock-in?

Liz: I can bake some cookies.

Brad: I'll make a pot of tamales.

Montana: I can bring some chips.

Rachel: That is so generous, Montana. Thank you.

Montana: Sure. It's not a big deal.

Rachel: But it is! And we thank you for it. Thank you.

Caleb: *(annoyed)* Could we move on?

Mr. Diaz: Good idea. We have one more meeting before the lock-in. We can finish our plans then. Let's do our Scripture reading.

Narrator: *(as Mr. Diaz exits)* When the group took a break later, Rachel stuck like glue to Montana.

Rachel: So how many rooms are in The Oaks?

Montana: I don't know. I haven't counted them. But I'll bet my mom has!

Rachel: I heard there's a pool in ... *(exits with Montana)*

Kellie: Maybe we were wrong about Rachel.

Caleb: Don't you get it? Rachel's interested in Montana because she lives at The Oaks.

Brad: But why? O-o-oh ... Montana has to be rich and important to live in a mansion like that.

Caleb: Right. Rachel won't give Mr. Stewart the time of day or talk to the other kids—or even treat salesclerks like human beings—but she will cozy up to someone with money and a big house.

Liz: That's terrible!

Caleb: *(snorts)* Hey, there's nobody like Rachel.

Kellie: Well, at least she's being nice to Montana.

Caleb: But she still has a problem. We're her friends. We *have* to help her.

Brad: How? We tried talking to her, and she just didn't get it.

Caleb: Then we'll try again.

Scene Eight

Narrator: *(as Rachel and Montana enter)* By the end of the evening, Rachel was acting like Montana was her best friend. *(snorts)* Ironic, huh? I mean … considering what she said before.

Caleb: It sure is.

Rachel: Hey, Montana, call me when you get home so we can talk some more.

Montana: OK. It was nice to meet you all.

Others: Bye! Later! *Etc.*

Caleb: So … Rachel … about Montana …

Rachel: Isn't she great? I really like her.

Caleb: But you didn't even want to talk to her when she first got here.

Rachel: I talked to her!

Kellie: Oh, sure.

Liz: You told her to go away.

Rachel: I did not!

Caleb: Well, not in so many words, but you weren't friendly. Then you found out Montana's rich, and you warmed right up to her.

Rachel: That's not true! I didn't know her, OK? And when I got to know her better, we started becoming friends.

Brad: So you don't care that she lives in a mansion?

Rachel: No! That's ridiculous! I'm friends with you guys, and your houses aren't that great.

Kellie: Excuse me?

Rachel: I'm sorry. I didn't mean it to come out like that. Listen. You all have known me for years. How can you think I'm a snob?

Caleb: Sometimes people change.

Rachel: Well, I haven't! Now I'd better go. See you later. *(exits)*

Brad: See? She just doesn't get it.

Caleb: Look, we know she's a good person inside. If she really understood how she's acting, she'd change. We can't give up on her.

Brad: We can't?

Caleb: Brad!

Brad: I mean ... we can't!

Scene Nine

Narrator: *(as all except Liz exit and Rachel enters)* Over the next week, the other kids didn't do much with Rachel. Whenever anybody called her, she was too busy to talk.

Liz: *(miming phone)* So I said—

Rachel: *(miming phone)* Sorry, Liz, but I have to go. I'm meeting Montana at the mall.

Liz: Oh. OK. Talk to you—

Rachel: *(hanging up)* Click!

Liz: —later. *(exits)*

Narrator: *(as Caleb and Brad enter)* Whenever they saw Rachel, she only talked about Montana.

Rachel: Blah blah blah Montana blah Montana blah blah, *Etc. (continuing as others speak)*

Caleb: Uh-huh ... Uh-huh ... Uh-huh ...

Brad: Uh-huh ... Uh-huh ... Uh-huh ...

Caleb: Uh-huh ... So have you been to The Oaks yet? Rachel? Rachel?

Rachel: Huh?

Caleb: Has Montana asked you over?

Rachel: No, but I'm sure she will soon. We're really blah blah blah Montana blah *Etc. (exiting)*

Brad: Brother!

Narrator: *(as Kellie and Liz enter)* She didn't even show up when they were all supposed to meet at the bookstore.

Kellie: Where is she?

Liz: We planned this two weeks ago.

Caleb: Right. *Before* she met Montana.

Brad: You know, Rachel never has time for us anymore.

Liz: I guess we're not as good as Montana. We aren't rich.

Kellie: Yeah. We don't have her kind of status.

Caleb: Montana isn't better than we are just because she has money. And, you know, I don't think Montana believes that either. Rachel's the one with the problem! But I think I know how to get Rachel to see the truth.

Kellie: You do?

Caleb: Yep. With a little help from good old Saint Clare. Everybody give me a dollar.

Brad: Dude. You don't have to pay saints to get their help.

Caleb: I know! But you do have to pay for books.

Scene Ten

Narrator: Caleb went over to Rachel's house to put his plan into action.

Rachel: Hey, Caleb. What's up?

Caleb: You didn't meet everybody at the bookstore.

Rachel: I'm sorry! Montana and I got to talking on the phone and—

Caleb: So, anyway … I got you a book.

Rachel: That's nice! Hmmmm … Saint Clare, huh?

Caleb: Her life story is fascinating. Her family was well-off and influential, and she had a fancy home and nice clothes and a cushy life.

Rachel: Sounds great!

Caleb: Yeah, but she didn't feel satisfied. Then she met Francis of Assisi, and she realized having nice things wasn't important. If her life was going to mean—

Rachel: Don't tell me the whole book!

Caleb: OK, I won't. But when you're reading, I want you to notice something about Saint Clare. She understood that it's not material things that make a person matter. She didn't value people for what they had—or look down on them for what they didn't have.

Rachel: Are you still on that? Look, Caleb, I treat everybody alike.

Caleb: No, you don't! And your friendship with Montana proves it. You weren't interested in her until you thought she was somebody rich. Now you can't wait to get invited to The Oaks!

Rachel: Because Montana is my friend! Hey, I'd better go call her back. Thanks for the book.

Caleb: Read it, OK? You might learn something. *(exits)*

Rachel: Yeah, right.

Scene Eleven

Narrator: Rachel *did* read the book later, just to prove Caleb wrong.

Rachel: He's nuts to think somebody like me could be a snob!

Narrator: Saint Clare's life *was* interesting. Rachel was amazed at how she gave up all her nice things to lead a group of religious sisters and live a poor life as Jesus did. They helped any needy people who knocked on their door, treating each one as they would treat Christ.

Rachel: That must have been hard! She could have married a rich man and gone on living in luxury. But she focused on God and helping the poor instead of on status or material things. She didn't even wear shoes!

Narrator: Rachel had to admit she was impressed with Saint Clare. But she didn't see why Caleb thought *she* needed to learn anything from the book.

Rachel: I'm not a saint, but I'm already a lot like Saint Clare. I don't care about material things either. Or status. Like it doesn't matter to me that Montana's rich. Not one bit!

Scene Twelve

Narrator: By the next youth group meeting, Montana still hadn't invited Rachel to her house. And Rachel thought she knew why not.

Rachel: I'll bet lots of people *do* like her just for her money and her position. I need to show her I'm a true friend.

Narrator: *(as Montana enters)* So when Montana arrived, Rachel took her to one side to talk.

Rachel: You know, you've been to my house, but I've never been to yours. I hope you understand I really want to be your friend.

Montana: I'm sorry! But Mom just started working at The Oaks and she doesn't think it's a good idea to have company yet.

Rachel: Hey, it's hard to move, but … Wait … What are you saying?

Montana: Sometimes people don't like a new housekeeper to have visitors at first, and Mom wants to respect that. But once the boss and his family adjust and Mom gets settled into a work schedule, I'll have you over, OK?

Rachel: Oh. OK. Great.

Montana: Are you all right? You look kind of pale.

Rachel: I'm fine. Let's sit down. The meeting is starting.

Scene Thirteen

Narrator: *(as Montana exits)* But Rachel wasn't fine. She was in shock.

Rachel: Montana's mom is the *housekeeper* at The Oaks! They're not rich! Her family probably has separate living quarters. She's might not even be allowed to show me around the mansion.

Narrator: At first, Rachel was overwhelmed with disappointment. Then another feeling crept in.

Rachel: Who cares if Montana asks me over? It's not like we can enjoy the place. And we sure won't be eating gourmet meals or sleeping in fancy bedrooms. Why waste my time with …

Narrator: Then a new … and horrible … feeling swept over Rachel.

Rachel: Oh, no! My friends are right! Montana is the same nice person she always was, but I'm acting like she's nobody now that I know she's not rich. And I thought I was like Saint Clare! Brother! I *am* a snob!

Narrator: Rachel couldn't pay attention to the meeting. She just sat there, remembering other times she treated people unfairly.

Rachel: I was too good to talk to Mr. Stewart! And how often have I been rude to clerks and waitresses? Before Montana, I hadn't made a new friend in forever. Nobody's ever good enough for me anymore! Man! Why would anybody *want* to be friends with somebody like me? I have to change my attitude. But … but can I?

Narrator: Then Rachel thought of Saint Clare.

Rachel: She completely changed her life with God's help. I know he'll help me, too. *(exits)*

Scene Fourteen

Narrator: Since that night, Rachel has really made some changes. Not that it's been easy! She has a hard time thinking of things to say to the people she used to look down on. And when she does talk to them, she has to work at sounding kind and respectful.

Rachel: *(entering with Caleb)* I can't believe I used to be so rude!

Caleb: But you're doing much better. And that's great.

Narrator: Sometimes Rachel really has to fight the feeling that somebody isn't worth her time. But she tries to be like Saint Clare and value what matters. And now that Rachel's treating people more equally, her friends thinks she's great. They have all kinds of nice things to say about her!

Liz, Brad, Kellie, and Montana: *("talking" to one another as they walk across stage then exit)* Blah blah blah Rachel blah Rachel, *Etc.*

Rachel: OK. I cannot understand them when they all talk at once.

Caleb: Well, I can tell you what they said.

Rachel: What?

Caleb: Blah blah blah Rachel blah Rachel, *Etc.*

Rachel: Oh, ha ha.

Caleb: OK, OK. What they really said was they're glad to know somebody like you. And you know what? So am I.

Rachel: *(as they exit)* Thanks, Caleb.

Narrator: She really *is* nice. Yeah … there's nobody like Rachel.

SAINT CLARE

Glad to Help!

SUMMARY

Cole thinks of himself as a helpful person, but he only does the jobs he wants to do. Could he learn a lesson from Saint Andrew Kim Daegeon about helping where you're needed?

COSTUMES/SETS/PROPS

All characters wear contemporary clothing.

A few tables and chairs can serve as home, school, and church.

Props can be mimed, and this is probably the easiest way to handle the craft items. However, if props are desired, the following can be used: stack of papers for the teacher, list and sign-up sheet for Mrs. Hutchison, materials for craft projects (paper, glue, clear plates, looms, weaving materials, cards, stamps, plastic bags), completed projects, cash box, and bags.

PRESENTATION

The other kids and adults should show they don't really find Cole that helpful.

In Scenes Five and Six, kids can mime making projects and Cole can mime "helping."

CAST

Narrator

Cole

Bianca, his sister

Teacher

Mrs. Hutchison, youth group sponsor

Youth group: Jin, Mallory, Grace, Isabella, Matthew, Susan, and Brett

Father Jasper

ABOUT SAINT ANDREW KIM DAEGEON

Andrew Kim Daegeon was born in 1821 in Korea. Andrew's parents, Catholic converts, raised their son in the faith. The government persecuted Christians, and many were martyred, including Andrew's father. As a teenager, Andrew went to Macao to study for the priesthood. After being ordained, he returned to Korea to help the Christians there. In less than a year, he was executed for trying to smuggle other priests into the country. His feast day in Korea is July 5. On September 20, he also shares a feast day with the other martyrs of Korea. He is the patron of the Korean clergy.

Glad to Help!

Scene One

Narrator: Cole thought of himself as a helpful person.

Cole: Yeah, that's me—helpful. Whenever somebody needs help with something … well … there I am … helping!

Narrator: Cole felt helping others was the right thing to do.

Cole: Yeah, helping others … That's what life is all about. That's what *I'm* all about.

Narrator: Of course, Cole tried to be helpful at home.

Bianca: *(entering)* Grandpa's visiting this weekend, so the guest room needs to be cleaned.

Cole: I'd be glad to help with that, Bianca. I'm going to get a dust cloth right now.

Bianca: We also need to vacuum, scour everything in the bathroom, put out new towels, mop—

Cole: I'm on those towels, Sis! You start the other jobs, and I'll get the towels. I mean … as soon as I finish the dusting.

Bianca: How long is that going to take?

Cole: I don't know, but don't worry. I'll do a good job. Aren't you glad I'm here to help?

Bianca: Yeah. Thrilled. *(exits)*

September/Glad to Help! 129

Scene Two

Narrator: Cole was helpful at school, too. When he finished his work early, he always asked the teacher for a job to do.

Teacher: *(entering)* Let's see ... How about taking the books off that shelf so we can move it across the room?

Cole: Are you sure you want to put the shelf over there? Maybe you should think on that.

Teacher: OK. You could clean out the hamster cage.

Cole: I could, but do I really have time before the bell?

Teacher: Probably, but maybe you'd rather start sorting these papers instead.

Cole: Wow. That's a big stack. Hey, the board needs to be erased. I'd better take care of that.

Teacher: All right then. And thanks, Cole.

Cole: I'm always glad to help!

Teacher: Uh-huh. *(exits)*

Scene Three

Narrator: *(as Mrs. Hutchison and youth group enter)* And Cole was helpful at church. Especially in youth group.

Mrs. Hutchison: OK, I think we're ready for our visit to the nursing home. Jin and Mallory are bringing refreshments. Brett, Isabella, and Grace are making gifts for the residents. Matthew and Susan are planning games. I think that's it.

Cole: You forgot me, Mrs. Hutchison.

Mrs. Hutchison: I don't see you on my list, Cole. What is it that you're doing?

Cole: Remember? I said I'd hold the door? As we go in?

Mrs. Hutchison: Oh, yes. I guess I forgot to write that down.

Jin: Gee. I wonder why.

Cole: It's not like Mrs. Hutchison needs to put my name down. She knows *I'll* be helping.

Mallory: Right.

Cole: Oh, and Mrs. Hutchison? I'll hold the door on our way *out,* too.

Mrs. Hutchison: Thank you, Cole.

Cole: Glad to help!

Grace: Brother.

Scene Four

Narrator: So Cole went along, helping out in his … um … helpful way and feeling pretty good about it. *Until* Isabella came up with the idea of having a craft fair.

Isabella: … So we make all these cute things and sell them in the parish center after the Masses one weekend. It's not our usual fundraiser, but I think people will support us.

Mrs. Hutchison: Great idea!

Matthew: I agree!

Susan: Me, too!

Others (except Cole): Yeah! Sounds good! Great idea! *Etc.*

Cole: It *seems* like a good idea, but maybe we should stick to what we know will work. I mean … we made a lot of money selling candy last year. I sold ten boxes myself.

Jin: You did not! Your parents sold all your candy at their jobs.

Cole: Parents are allowed to help! And anyway … I'm thinking it'll be a lot of work to make all that stuff.

Isabella: But everybody will help.

Brett: *(muttering)* Not everybody.

Cole: And what are we going to make, anyway?

Isabella: I have a great craft book at home. It has directions for lots of easy, fun projects. I could look through that and get together some ideas before our next meeting.

Mrs. Hutchison: That's wonderful. Thank you, Isabella.

Cole: Well, making the stuff isn't all there is to it. We'll have to advertise and set up and—

Jin: Look, if you don't want to help …

Cole: Of course, I want to help! I'm always glad to help!

Matthew: Then let's do it.

Others (except Cole): Yeah! Let's do it! *Etc.*

Mrs. Hutchison: All right. We'll look forward to your report next time, Isabella. And thank you, dear, for getting that together.

Isabella: Oh, I'm always glad to help.

Cole: *(muttering as others exit)* Copycat.

Scene Five

Narrator: Cole wasn't enthused about the craft fair, but he still planned to help.

Cole: Hey, that's the kind of person I am.

Narrator: Uh-huh.

Cole: I mean … some people think they're so-o-o helpful, but being helpful is more than thinking up ideas of stuff for other people to do, you know.

Narrator: Right. So Isabella came to the next meeting with lots of ideas for craft projects.

Cole: *(snorts)* Big deal.

Narrator: *(as Mrs. Hutchison and youth group enter)* Once the group decided which ideas to use, they scheduled a day to work on the projects.

Mrs. Hutchison: OK, everybody. Let's see how much we can accomplish today. Isabella, could you explain the setup?

Isabella: Sure. Over by the windows, we have materials for the cookie plates. You carefully glue the little bits of paper all over the back of each clear plate. Turn them so the color shows through. Oh, and don't leave any bare spots, OK?

Cole: Man. That's going to take forever to do.

Grace: But they'll look nice when we're finished.

Isabella: In the middle of the room, we'll make the potholders. Be sure to string the loom with contrasting colors and weave carefully and tightly. We want these to be quality potholders.

Cole: Selling candy is a lot easier than weaving.

Jin: Especially when someone else does it for you.

Cole: Look, I helped my parents.

Mrs. Hutchison: Of course, you did, Cole. Isabella?

Isabella: The last project is over by the door. Stamp the design on each card. When you have ten cards finished, put them in a plastic bag.

Mrs. Hutchison: OK, everybody choose a project and get to work.

Narrator: Brett and Isabella went to work on the plates, Jin and Mallory started weaving, and everybody else headed for the card-making table. Cole just stood there. Doing nothing.

Cole: Well, I'm thinking about how I can help.

Narrator: Dude … plates, potholders, or cards.

Cole: I know, OK? I think I'll help with … the potholders.

Narrator: Really? That seems like a hard job.

Cole: Definitely. That's why Jin and Mallory need my help.

Narrator: So Cole went to help out at the potholder table.

Cole: I'll hand the loops to you, OK?

Jin: But they're right here on the table. Like right next to us.

Mallory: Yeah, we can get them ourselves.

Cole: But if I hand them to you, you won't *have* to pick them up yourselves.

Jin: *(sarcastic)* Gee, thanks, Cole, but—

Cole: You guys don't have to thank me. I'm glad to help!

Scene Six

Narrator: It took several work sessions to get all the projects finished.

Cole: Even with my help!

Narrator: *(sarcastic)* Yes. Incredible, isn't it? *(to audience)* Cole handed out weaving loops and told people when they left a bare spot on a cookie plate and counted the cards as people made them, but … amazingly … it took a while to make enough items for the fair.

Mrs. Hutchison: The projects look great! You all did such a good job.

Matthew: Isabella made it easy!

Susan: Yeah. She found good projects for us to do.

Grace: And she got the supplies.

Brett: And organized them!

Mrs. Hutchison: You really *were* a big help, Isabella. Thanks so much.

Isabella: You're welcome. And I want to thank you all for your hard work.

Cole: You're welcome. I was glad to help!

Jin: *(muttering)* Give me a break.

Mrs. Hutchison: The fair is scheduled for the twentieth. What do we need to do to get ready?

Isabella: I think we should advertise. I could write up something for the church bulletin. Oh, and I could draw an ad for the school newspaper.

Mallory: Good idea! And we'll need to set up before the first Mass. I can do that.

Isabella: I'll help you.

Mallory: Thanks.

Mrs. Hutchison: Great! I thought we'd take turns working the fair so I made this sign-up sheet.

Isabella: I can help after all the Masses, Mrs. Hutchison.

Cole: So can I!

Mrs. Hutchison: I don't think anyone needs to help out after *every* Mass. We can share—

Isabella: But I'd be glad to help after all the Masses.

Cole: Not as glad as I'd be. I mean … I'd *love* to do it.

Isabella: I know what you mean. Helping is just so satisfying, isn't it?

Cole: *(snorts)* Satisfying? Helping is my life!

Jin: *(muttering)* Heaven help *us*!

Mrs. Hutchison: Everybody sign up for the times you want to come. If you want to help after all the Masses, well … thank you.

Isabella, Cole: Glad to help!

Scene Seven

Narrator: *(as others exit)* Cole came to the fair ready to work hard, but he hardly got a chance to help at all.

Cole: That annoying Isabella! She just has to do everything!

Jin: *(entering)* Why are you standing here doing nothing?

Cole: That annoying Isabella! She just has to do everything!

Jin: What do you mean?

Cole: She greets people as they come in and she takes their money and she makes change and she puts their stuff in bags. She does everything!

Jin: You could greet people.

Cole: But they walk by the money table as they come in. Isabella gets to them first!

Jin: OK. Why don't you help with the money?

Cole: She has the cash box right in front of her!

Jin: OK then. Bag stuff for people.

Cole: It's so hard to get those plastic bags open! You rub the plastic between your fingers, but you can't find an opening, and it's just a big pain. I hate that!

Jin: O. Kay. I'm going to go help Isabella put stuff in bags. *(exits)*

Cole: *(calling after him)* Hey, good luck with that!

Narrator: So Cole just stood around, not helping at all.

Cole: I'm … I'm watching to be sure nothing gets stolen. That's helpful!

Narrator: *(as Mrs. Hutchison and Father Jasper enter)* Right. After Cole had guarded the tables awhile, Mrs. Hutchison came in with Father Jasper. They looked around, and when they got close to Cole, he could hear their conversation.

Father Jasper: This is great! It must have taken a lot of work to pull together a project like this.

Mrs. Hutchison: Thanks, Father. You know, all the kids worked on this, but Isabella was a real blessing! She not only came up with the idea of the fair, but she's also been a tremendous help with everything! I've never had such a helpful child in the group.

Father Jasper: Wonderful!

Cole: *(as Mrs. Hutchison and Father Jasper exit)* Sheesh! It's not like Isabella's the only person doing anything! Hey, Father Jasper is talking to her! And Mrs. Hutchison, too. I'll bet they're saying how helpful she is. They didn't mention anything about me standing here, keeping an eye on stuff. That's just as helpful as what Isabelle's doing!

Narrator: Yeah, and what's the point in being helpful if nobody notices, huh?

Cole: Yeah! I mean ... no! It's just not fair for her to get all the credit. And look at her! She thinks she's big stuff, that Little Miss I'm-More-Helpful-Than-Anybody-Else. Like this is all about her! I don't think she really understands what being helpful means. Maybe I can help her with that.

Scene Eight

Narrator: *(as Isabella enters)* After the craft fair, Cole went up to Isabella, planning to talk to her about her attitude.

Isabella: Hi, Cole! Mrs. Hutchison took the cash box with her, but I think we made a lot of money. Just think of all the people we'll be able to help!

Cole: You're really big on helping, aren't you?

Isabella: You bet!

Cole: That's great, but, you know, helping is about helping other people to help them, not about helping other people to help yourself.

Isabella: I think I need some help to understand what you just said.

Cole: What I mean is ... you don't help other people just to make yourself look good.

Isabella: Why, thank you, Cole! I really am sincere about helping others more than I used to be, and it's so nice of you to notice.

Cole: Wait. I didn't—

Isabella: Do you know why I decided to be more helpful?

Cole: Look, I ... I mean ... no.

Isabella: It's because of Saint Andrew Kim Daegeon. Have you ever heard of him?

Cole: I don't think so.

Isabella: My dad just got back from his tour of duty in Korea. While he was there, he really got inspired by Saint Andrew. So when he returned home, he told me all about him.

Cole: Uh-huh. Listen, I was—

Isabella: See, Saint Andrew Kim Daegeon lived in Korea long ago, when Christianity wasn't allowed there. But some people learned about Jesus from books and from missionaries, and they lived as Christians anyway. They were terribly mistreated for their faith, and many were killed. Life was tough for Korean Christians, and the people really, really needed some priests to help them.

Cole: That's interesting. Look, Isabella, helping other people is very important.

Isabella: Saint Andrew Kim Daegeon thought so, too! When he was just a teenager, he went to Macao to study for the priesthood so he could help others. And when he became a priest, he went where he was really needed—back to Korea!

Cole: Wait. Didn't you say Christians were being martyred there?

Isabella: Yes. But Saint Andrew wanted to help his people even if it put his life in danger. He devoted himself to the Church in Korea, but after less than a year he was executed for trying to smuggle more priests into the country.

Cole: Wow. That's sad.

Isabella: Yeah. When I heard about him, I felt like I had to do more, you know? Like, if he could risk so much to help others, why couldn't I be more helpful in my life? Hey, it looks like Jin and Susan need help taking down that table. *(exits)*

Cole: Maybe I was wrong about her. She really cares about helping. Like me!

Scene Nine

Narrator: Then Cole looked around and noticed something. Except for the last table, all the others had been taken down and stacked. The leftover craft items were packed in boxes to be saved for the next fair. The floor had been swept, the trash was bagged, and—

Cole: And I didn't help do any of that! I did check the windows to see if they were locked, but we never opened them, so how helpful was that?

Narrator: Not very.

Cole: No kidding. But I didn't want to lift those heavy tables or sweep or any of that other stuff. So I just helped the way I wanted to help. But ... like I told Isabella ... helping others is helping *them,* not yourself, because if you're just helping yourself, then it's not really helping.

Narrator: Um ... help! What are you saying?

Cole: It's like Saint Andrew Kim Daegeon. He helped where he was really needed, even though it was hard and dangerous. He didn't just do easy stuff. *(sighs)* Like I do. If I don't like a job, I don't do it. If I can find an easy way, I take it. I keep acting like I'm helpful, but I'm really not!

Susan: *(entering with Jin)* We're finished with the work now, so you can stop checking windows.

Jin: Yeah. And thanks so much for all your help. *(exits with Susan)*

Cole: And everybody knows it!

Scene Ten

Narrator: When you realize you're not the person you thought you were, it can be tough. The more Cole thought about all the unhelpful ways he'd been helping, the worse he felt. But finally he thought of something that could help him feel better.

Cole: I have to change. I have to start helping others for real!

Narrator: Of course, people had to adjust to the new Cole.

Bianca: *(entering)* You're going to clean the whole kitchen?

Cole: Yeah.

Bianca: I don't know what you're trying to pull, but I'm leaving before you change your mind! *(exits)*

Teacher: *(entering)* Could you erase that board, Cole?

Cole: Sure! I'll bet I could get those papers sorted before the bell, too.

Teacher: OK. Thanks.

Cole: And I'll come early tomorrow and clean the hamster cage.

Teacher: Do you need to go see the nurse?

Cole: No, I'm fine. I just really want to help.

Teacher: OK. Well ... thank you, Cole. *(exits)*

Narrator: *(as Mrs. Hutchison and youth group enter)* And Cole surprised people at church with his new helpfulness. Especially at youth group.

Mrs. Hutchison: Our Study Buddy program starts Monday. Who can help with that?

Cole: I can! I can!

Matthew: Put him down for holding the door open.

Grace: Or holding up the wall.

Brett: Or breathing. That'd be a big help.

Other kids: *(laugh)*

Mrs. Hutchison: That's enough of that!

Cole: It's OK, Mrs. Hutchison. I know I haven't been much help before, but I'm hoping to change that. So I'd be glad to tutor a first-grader. You can count on me.

Isabella: That's great!

Jin: Wow. Do you really mean it, Cole?

Cole: Yes. I want to do better. And if I start slacking off again, maybe you guys could … you know … let me know. OK?

Jin: Sure. We'd be … *(looking at others)*

Others: Glad to help!

SAINT ANDREW
KIM DAEGEON

Big Enough

SUMMARY

Josie is tired of being a little person. Just once, she wants to do something big! But could it be that little things mean more than she realizes?

COSTUMES/SETS/PROPS

All characters wear contemporary clothing.

A table and some chairs should suffice for all the locations in the play.

If props are desired, the following can be used: some papers for Mr. Washington, campaign posters, books and notebooks for kids, paper and pencil for Josie, and a book about Saint Thérèse (or Josie's script can be covered to look like such a book).

PRESENTATION

In Scene Four, actors can pretend the sign-up list is posted between them and the audience.

Josie mopes through Scene Eight.

In Scene Nine, she can mime reading and writing.

CAST

Narrator

Josie

Bill

Maya

Kareem

Alexis, Josie's best friend

Mr. Washington, homeroom and science teacher

Student One

Student Two

Student Three

ABOUT SAINT THÉRÈSE OF LISIEUX

Thérèse was born in France in 1873. She led a pampered
childhood but suffered terribly when her mother died and when
her sister Pauline later left home to join a Carmelite convent. Thérèse developed a
strong spiritual life, and, longing to devote herself to Jesus, she entered her sister's
convent at age fifteen. There she lived her "little way," making small sacrifices with
great love for God. On the order of her superior, Thérèse wrote her autobiography,
Story of a Soul, which was published after her death and has inspired thousands.
Thérèse was twenty-four when she died from tuberculosis. Her feast day is October 1.
She is the patron of missionaries.

Big Enough

Scene One

Narrator: Some people are big. They have big adventures. They put on big shows. They accomplish big things. Everybody knows them so even their names are big. Josie wasn't one of those people.

Josie: I'm just a little nobody who does little things with my little life.

Narrator: You sound unhappy.

Josie: *(snorts)* Just a little!

Narrator: *(as Bill, Maya, Kareem, and Alexis enter)* Josie tried to make something big happen. In youth group, she volunteered to be the treasurer.

Josie: Now there's a big job.

Narrator: But several people wanted to be treasurer.

Bill: I can do it! I'm a hard worker.

Maya: I'm organized.

Kareem: I'm good at math.

Josie: I'm … um … Josie.

Narrator: But the youth group sponsor chose Kareem for the job.

Josie: *(to Alexis)* Darn it! I really wanted to be the treasurer.

Alexis: I know. But there are other things you can do to help out.

Josie: Yeah. Little, unimportant things.

Scene Two

Narrator: *(as Mr. Washington enters)* And Josie tried to get an important job in her homeroom.

Mr. Washington: Bill, would you take these crucial, life-or-death papers to the office?

Bill: Yes, sir.

Mr. Washington: And, Maya, would you mind taking on the awesome responsibility of caring for the living creatures we keep as classroom pets?

Maya: No problem, Mr. Washington.

Josie: Can I help with something?

Mr. Washington: Could you throw that piece of paper away? The one on the floor there?

Josie: You mean that little speck? That's not paper. That's lint.

Mr. Washington: Could you take care of it?

Josie: *(sighs)* Yes, sir. I think I can handle it.

Alexis: It's really nice of you to help Mr. Washington.

Josie: Right. What would he do without me?

Scene Three

Narrator: *(as Mr. Washington exits)* Josie even tried out for a play at school.

Josie: I'm going out for the biggest, most important role.

Alexis: The queen?

Josie: No—the narrator!

Narrator: It's about time somebody appreciated … um … Several people tried out for that part.

Bill: Once upon a time …

Maya: In a faraway land …

Kareem: There lived a powerful queen …

Josie: Who. Ruled. Her. Kingdom. With. Great. Merky.

Alexis: *(to Josie)* Psst! That's "mercy."

Josie: Oh. Who. Ruled. Her. Kingdom. With. Great. Mercy.

Narrator: *(as Bill, Maya, and Kareem exit)* But when the cast list was posted, Josie found she was playing a tree.

Josie: That's the smallest part! The tree doesn't even have any lines.

Alexis: Well, at least you got in. Some of us—

Josie: I'm tired of being a little person doing little things. Just once, I want to do something big.

Narrator: Suddenly, a really good idea hit Josie.

Josie: He-e-ey. I should run for student council. Representing my whole grade … now that would be big. A student council representative is really somebody.

Alexis: And student council helps make our school a better place.

Josie: It does? I mean … sure it does.

Scene Four

Narrator: So Josie went to the office bulletin board and signed up to run for student council.

Josie: Wow. Four other people in our grade are running, too.

Alexis: But you have just as good a chance to win as anybody.

Josie: Maybe you're right.

Narrator: Then some other kids came along and took a look at the list.

Student One: Who's this José?

Student Two: We don't have a José in our grade level.

Alexis: You're reading that name wrong.

Student Three: Oh, yeah. It says … let me look closer … "Joz-ra." What kind of name is that?

Josie: It's not Joz-ra. It's Josie.

Student Three: Oh. I see it now.

Student Two: You're right. It does say "Josie."

Student One: So who's Josie?

Alexis: She's—

Josie: Never mind, Alexis. *(as others exit)* Of course, they don't know who I am. I've never done anything important around here. But I'm going to run a huge campaign, and everybody will know who I am, and then I'll get elected, and I'll finally be big! Big, I say!

Alexis: O. Kay.

Josie: *(embarrassed by outburst)* So … um … could you help me make some campaign posters?

Alexis: *(joking)* Sure. Do you want them to be BIG?

Josie: *(laughing)* Yeah. That'd be great.

Scene Five

Narrator: That afternoon, Josie and Alexis made a huge stack of campaign posters.

Josie: Maybe this is a waste of time. Somebody like me couldn't possibly win.

Alexis: Yes, you could! And these posters will help. Let's go to school early tomorrow and plaster the walls.

Josie: I have my first play rehearsal before school tomorrow.

Alexis: OK then, I'll put them up while you're at the rehearsal.

Josie: Thanks!

Narrator: *(as Alexis exits)* So Josie went to rehearsal the next morning and sat around the whole time because they never got to her scene in the play.

Josie: Like I was going to get to say anything anyway!

Narrator: She was feeling pretty discouraged when she came out of the rehearsal, but then she saw that Alexis had hung campaign posters everywhere.

Josie: Wow! Now I look like somebody important.

Student One: *(entering with Students Two and Three)* Look at all these posters! Who *is* this Josie person?

Josie: I'm Josie. And I want to be your student council representative.

Student Two: Why?

Josie: Um ... I ... Because ... I want to make this school a better place?

Student Three: Right.

Student One: *(to friends as they exit)* That's what all the politicians say when they want your vote. But do they *really* care about the little people?

Josie: Wow. Posters aren't going to be enough to win this election. I'll have to actually produce some actual ideas.

Scene Six

Narrator: Josie tried to think of a big idea to impress everybody into voting for her.

Josie: I must have a little brain, too, because I can't come up with anything.

Narrator: *(as all other kids enter)* But at lunch Josie got some real inspiration.

Bill: I stayed up late last night to study.

Maya: Me, too.

Bill: Why did Mr. Washington have to give us a science test on the same day Ms. Monaco scheduled a quiz on irregular verbs and Mr. James is testing us on fractions?

Alexis: I don't know. It sure makes things hard when they do that.

Kareem: Yeah, but I guess there's nothing anybody can do about it.

Josie: Really! It's not like we can change anything that goes on around here.

Maya: If that's how you feel, then why are you running for student council?

Josie: Well, I ... See I'm ... I mean ... Wait. A. Minute. That's it!

Alexis: What?

Josie: The big idea I need! Listen, everybody, I'm running for student council because I do believe we can change things. *(stands and begins to orate)* Yes, we *can* make a change for the better! Sure, we're little people in this big old school, but when little people get together they can make ... um ... a big group of little people! And a big group can do something!

Student One: There she goes again.

Student Two: Yeah. She talks, but she doesn't say much, does she?

Student Three: Why should we vote for her?

Josie: Because I really do have a big idea. I think the teachers should have a testing calendar in the office. Whenever they want to give a test, they sign up on the calendar. If there's already a test scheduled that day, they have to choose another time. That way we won't be overloaded.

Other kids: Wow! Great idea! I like it! *Etc.*

Student One: What was her name?

Student Two: Josie. I'm going to vote for her.

Student Three: Me, too. Josie! Josie!

Other kids: *(joining in as all except Alexis exit)* Josie! Josie!

Alexis: I think you're going to win.

Josie: Finally! Finally I'll be somebody!

Alexis: You're already somebody.

Josie: Not really. But soon I will be.

Scene Seven

Narrator: The idea of winning the election made Josie feel better than she had in a long time.

Josie: And bigger!

Narrator: She got tons of good feedback on her test schedule idea.

Josie: Yep! Everybody's starting to look up to me thanks to my big idea!

Narrator: And she felt confident she had the election in the bag.

Josie: I'm going to win big!

Narrator: *(as Mr. Washington, Bill, Maya, Kareem, and Alexis enter)* Yes, Josie thought she was BIG stuff, but when the BIG day came around, she got a BIG surprise.

Mr. Washington: Now before I announce the results of the election, I want to say that all the candidates are winners in my book. OK ... our new student council representative is ... Bill.

Everyone except Josie: *(as all except Josie and Alexis exit)* Way to go! Congratulations! *Etc.*

Alexis: *(to Josie)* I'm sorry, Josie. I know this meant a lot to you.

Josie: Yeah. How stupid was that? Like little old nobody me could ever be any kind of big somebody. *(exits)*

Alexis: But, Josie … She's really upset. Maybe I can help her feel better. *(exits)*

Narrator: Now there's a big job!

Scene Eight

Narrator: *(as Josie enters)* Josie decided she was going to be a little person all her life, so what was the point in even trying?

Josie: I'm always going to be a little person, so what's the point in even trying?

Narrator: So she gave up.

Josie: I'm giving up.

Narrator: She decided to accept being a nobody.

Josie: I'm nobody and I might as well accept that.

Narrator: *(without moving lips)* Stop copying me.

Josie: *(without moving lips)* Make me.

Narrator: So … anyway … Josie was a big, annoying dope.

Josie: I'm a … he-e-ey …

Narrator: Alexis felt really sorry for her friend, and she tried to cheer her up.

Alexis: *(entering)* You still have the play to look forward to.

Josie: I quit the play.

Alexis: But why?

Josie: I. Was. A. Tree. With no lines.

Alexis: Well, you know what they say: there are no little parts … just little actors.

Josie: OK, here's my part. *(poses as tree for a moment, waves branches a bit, drops arms)* That is a little part, Alexis. So little they can do the play without me.

Alexis: Wait. Doesn't the tree turn into a golden rock at the end?

Josie: A golden rock with no lines!

Alexis: Oh. Hey, I heard Mr. Washington talking about rearranging the lab area. That sounds like an important job, huh? Maybe you could help.

Josie: I don't think so. I'm too busy with my lint-picking responsibilities.

Alexis: Well, we need to raise money in youth group. Maybe you could be in charge of that.

Josie: Why should I? We have a treasurer, don't we?

Alexis: Yeah, I guess we do. I know! Why don't you enter the contest Ms. Monaco told us about? You know … where you write a prayer to a saint and the winners get put in a book?

Josie: Right. Like anybody is going to publish something I write.

Alexis: They might. And wouldn't it be really cool if they did? I mean … a published author … That's BIG! Right?

Josie: I guess. OK, I'll give it a try.

Alexis: Great! *(exits)*

Josie: Brother. I thought she'd never leave me alone.

Narrator: Wait. Are you going to write the prayer?

Josie: She'll be asking about it so I guess I have to. But I'm going to make it a little one.

Scene Nine

Narrator: Josie went to the library and looked at the books about saints.

Josie: Hmmm … Which saint should I write the prayer to? Oh, here's a good one. The LITTLE Flower of Jesus. That's perfect for me.

Narrator: Josie sat down, planning to read up on the saint a bit, then dash something off for the contest.

Josie: OK. Saint Thérèse of Lisieux. The Little Flower of Jesus. Page One.

Narrator: Josie read about Thérèse's childhood first.

Josie: Gee. She was kind of spoiled. But that was sad how her mother died when she was little.

Narrator: Then she learned that Thérèse became a Carmelite sister at fifteen years old.

Josie: Wow. That was young!

Narrator: And then she found out something surprising about Saint Thérèse.

Josie: Hey, she felt like a little person, too! *And* she wished she could do something big. Like she really wanted to do great deeds for God. But she wasn't big and strong and powerful, so she just had to live her little life in the convent. I'll bet she was as disappointed as I am.

Narrator: But as Josie read on, she learned that Saint Thérèse had a special way of looking at life.

Josie: She believed little things could be really important—if you did them with love. So she tried to do everything—even chores!—with love for God. And she made little sacrifices like taking the smallest piece of bread … or talking to somebody annoying … or not complaining about stuff. Every little thing was a way to show God how much she loved him.

Narrator: Interesting, huh?

Josie: Yeah, but I guess that kind of thing works when you're a saint in the olden times. Nobody wants to live like that today. I mean … hardly anybody even noticed Thérèse.

Narrator: God did, didn't he?

Josie: Well, sure. I'm just saying you have to be somebody big to make it in modern times. OK now. What kind of prayer can I write? "Oh, Saint Thérèse … um … pray for me. Amen." There! That should get Alexis off my back.

Scene Ten

Narrator: But things went terribly wrong when Alexis read Josie's prayer.

Alexis: That's cool, Josie. Who knows? Maybe you'll win.

Josie: Look, I know you're just trying to be nice. That prayer isn't going to win anything.

Alexis: Well, I like it. It's simple, but it has … um … a big idea behind it.

Josie: Oh, it does not! Nothing is big about me or anything I do. Just accept the truth—I have! I'm just a little nobody and I always will be.

Alexis: No, you're not nobody and you're never … not … neither … I mean …

Josie: You know what your problem is? If you admit I'm a little nobody, then you'll have to admit you're a little nobody, too.

Alexis: What do you mean?

Josie: Well, you never do anything big in youth group, do you? And teachers don't give you important responsibilities, either. And what happened with the play? You didn't get a part at all—not even the tree. And who'd vote for you if you ran for student council?

Alexis: I . . . I can't believe you said that!

Josie: I'm just trying to help you out.

Alexis: Gee, that's big of you.

Josie: Well, I *am* your best friend.

Alexis: Not anymore you're not! *(exits)*

Josie: Well, that was kind of dramatic. I guess some people just can't handle the truth.

Scene Eleven

Narrator: After that, Josie and Alexis didn't speak for days, but they still saw each other everywhere. Which gave Josie the chance to notice something about her friend.

Josie: Ex-friend. And what's to notice?

Narrator: In youth group, Alexis didn't lead the prayers or read the Scripture aloud or do anything important at all.

Josie: Like I said: what's to notice? All she did was bookmark our Bibles before the meeting and talk to that obnoxious Brittany at the break.

Narrator: And in homeroom?

Josie: What about homeroom? She alphabetized Mr. Washington's ungraded papers. He didn't ask her to do it, but she did it anyway. Big deal.

Narrator: Uh-huh. Then Josie noticed Alexis doing the same thing for other teachers.

Josie: I wonder why . . . Oh, maybe it makes it easier later on when they're recording the grades in their grade books. I . . . I'll bet that really helps.

Narrator: Josie also found out that Alexis was taking care of the props for the play.

Josie: I didn't even think about props.

Narrator: And Josie often observed Alexis holding open a door for somebody or picking up trash or talking to people who weren't popular or—

Josie: OK, OK!

Narrator: And Josie remembered all the nice little things Alexis had done for her, too. Like helping her with the election. And trying to cheer her up. And being the best friend ever.

Josie: She … she really is a nice person.

Narrator: A nice *little* person? She never does anything big.

Josie: Oh, yes, she does! She's kind of like Saint Thérèse in a way. I mean … Alexis does all these little things—stuff that people hardly even notice—but it all makes life easier for others. That's big. That's huge! And I told her she was a nobody!

Narrator: A little nobody like you … that's what you said.

Josie: Well … I have been acting … um … little. But now I'm going to do something important.

Scene Twelve

Narrator: *(as Alexis enters)* So Josie apologized to Alexis. It wasn't the greatest apology ever …

Josie: That stuff I said … you were just … and I appreciate that … I mean …

Narrator: But Josie did manage to say those two little words that make such a big difference.

Josie: I'm sorry.

Alexis: It's OK. I know you were just upset.

Josie: But I shouldn't have … I mean … it's just … Thanks. So … want to hear my new prayer for the contest?

Alexis: Sure!

Josie: "Oh, Saint Thérèse, Little Flower,
　　　　help me remember every hour
　　　　little things can mean so much
　　　　so I can live with a loving touch
　　　　and understand that no one's small.
　　　　Not when God loves us all! Amen."

Alexis: I like it! You really might win the contest. And I'm not just saying that.

Josie: Thanks. But it's OK if I don't win.

Alexis: *(joking)* Oh. So it's not a BIG deal if you don't make it BIG and become a BIG somebody?

Josie: *(laughing)* Not really. As long as I have a good friend in my life, I'll be big enough.

SAINT
THÉRÈSE OF LISIEUX

Long-Distance Partners

SUMMARY

In social studies, Dante gets stuck with the worst partner of all. Chelsea drives him nuts about their project on Peru, and, even worse, tries to be his friend. How can he get rid of her?

COSTUMES/SETS/PROPS

All characters can wear contemporary clothing.

A few tables and chairs can be used for the classroom and cafeteria.

The following props may be used: a list for Chelsea (Scene Four), lunch trays, reference books for Dante's research, and papers for Chelsea's part of the project.

PRESENTATION

Chelsea talks quickly, running on and on without pauses.

In Scene Three, Mrs. Fox should show she's tired of Chelsea.

In Scene Seven, Chelsea might enter from different sides as Dante literally turns around.

CAST

Narrator

Dante

Chelsea

Porter, Dante's friend

Mrs. Fox, teacher

Other students: Jed, Annamarie, and Luke

ABOUT SAINT MARTIN DE PORRES

Martin de Porres was born in 1579 in Lima, Peru, the child of a freed slave and a Spanish nobleman. His father helped Martin and his sister get some schooling but did little else for them, leaving his family to live in poverty. At age twelve, Martin was apprenticed to a barber-surgeon who taught him some medical skills. After this training, Martin became a servant in a monastery and later a religious brother. He spent his life caring for the sick and needy without regard for their race or position in society. Many people, rich and poor, mourned Martin's death in 1639. His feast day is November 3. He is the patron of African-Americans and hairdressers.

Long-Distance Partners

Scene One

Narrator: Dante had been lucky so far, but, you know, when teachers keep making you do projects with other kids … Well … you're going to get stuck with a bad partner sometimes.

Dante: Bad? Right. I got stuck with the worst partner ever!

Narrator: You mean … ?

Dante: *(dreary)* Yes. It's Chelsea.

Chelsea: *(entering)* Isn't this great we get to do Peru for our project that is such a cool country I can't wait to find out everything about it how about you?

Dante: Huh? I mean … sure.

Chelsea: Our project is going to be fantastic I just know it and everybody will be so impressed I mean this is our chance to *Peru-ve* ourselves get it we can *prove* ourselves see it's a joke.

Dante: I get it.

Chelsea: I'm so glad Mrs. Fox put us together I think we'll make a great team I'm going to start looking up stuff about Peru right this second! *(exits)*

Dante: Yeah, you … um … do that. Man. I don't think I can stand working with her.

Narrator: But you have to do it. Once Mrs. Fox assigns partners, she never lets people change.

Dante: *(dreary)* Yeah. I am powerless. And doomed. Severely doomed.

Scene Two

Narrator: Dante might have lost all hope if it weren't for his friend Porter.

Porter: *(entering)* I got Jed for a partner. He's actually traveled in France so … what's wrong?

Dante: Bad news, man. Really, really, really bad news.

Porter: Oh, no! Is it really bad?

Dante: What did I say? Really, really, really bad news, OK?

Porter: OK. So what is it?

Dante: I got Chelsea for my partner. There is no way I can work with her. I'll go nuts!

Porter: She's not all bad. I mean … she's … um … cheerful.

Dante: So? Remember Julius? He was her partner for the state projects we did in second grade?

Porter: Sure. What about him?

Dante: One day he was there, and the next day … poof! We never saw him again.

Porter: Wait. Didn't his family move away?

Dante: Yep. Just so he didn't have to finish that project with Chelsea.

Porter: Oh, you don't know that!

Dante: I don't have proof, but it happened. And what about that Ellen girl? The one who got suspended for punching that kid last year? She did it because Chelsea was her lab partner.

Porter: She did not! Look, you'll work things out with Chelsea.

Dante: The only way I can work with Chelsea is by long distance.

Porter: So why don't you do that? Just split up the project. You can each work on your own and put it all together at the end.

Dante: That is a great idea! You just saved my life!

Porter: Get real. Chelsea isn't dangerous, you know.

Dante: Yeah, but she's so annoying it's scary.

Porter: Whatever.

Scene Three

Narrator: *(as Chelsea, Mrs. Fox, and others enter)* Dante decided to put Porter's great plan into action the next day when Mrs. Fox gave the class time to work on their projects.

Mrs. Fox: Remember—these projects count for half of your grade. Any questions?

Chelsea, Jed, Annamarie, and Luke: *(raise hands)*

Mrs. Fox: Jed?

Jed: Is it OK to bring in souvenirs from my trip to France?

Mrs. Fox: That would be great. Annamarie?

Annamarie: How about serving foods from our country?

Mrs. Fox: Sure. Talk to me later about when you want to do that. Luke?

Luke: I forgot my question.

Mrs. Fox: Well, maybe you'll think of it later. So let's get busy, everybody.

Chelsea: Mrs. Fox! Mrs. Fox!

Mrs. Fox: *(sighs)* Yes, Chelsea.

Chelsea: So when you say this is half of our grade did you mean for this grading period or for the whole semester because if it's—

Mrs. Fox: This grading period! I meant this grading period!

Chelsea: So this is big not as big as it would be if it counted as half of a semester grade but still this is an important project right if we want—

Mrs. Fox: Yes, it's important.

Chelsea: So if we—

Mrs. Fox: We'd better get started, Chelsea.

Annamarie: Please.

Luke: Yeah!

Jed: Before we run out of time!

Chelsea: OK well I'm sure we'll have *Samoa* time for questions later get it we'll have *some more*—

Dante: We get it! We get it!

Scene Four

Narrator: *(as all except Chelsea and Dante exit)* Dante took control of the situation as soon as he sat down with Chelsea.

Chelsea: OK so I made a list of everything we need to do for our project I think we should—

Dante: Let's split up your list, OK? We'll each work on our parts alone ... by ourselves ... and then we'll combine everything later. It'll be really efficient.

Chelsea: Well I don't know about that I think we need to work together because how—

Dante: Listen ... let's look at your list and just see if we can split things up.

Chelsea: OK I guess it wouldn't hurt to look I'm not saying—

Dante: Why don't you write about Peru's government and economy, and I'll write about the geography and history? And I'll draw the map and you can draw the flag.

Chelsea: But I—

Dante: No, I insist! You have to do the flag because you're such a good artist.

Chelsea: Why thank you Dante that is so nice of you I think you're the first person who's ever—

Dante: Right. So let's get busy, OK?

Chelsea: OK and we can *Czech* back with each other later get it *Czech* like the *Czech Republic* it's a joke I'm glad we didn't get that country because—

Dante: See you later! *(exits)*

Chelsea: *(to Narrator)* He's going to be a good partner I can tell he's really organized and he's nice too really nice don't you think?

Narrator: Um ... sure.

Chelsea: *(exiting)* Who knows maybe we'll actually become friends it could happen since ...

Scene Five

Narrator: *(as Dante, Porter, Jed, Annamarie, and Luke enter)* The long-distance plan worked great at first. Why, Chelsea didn't bother Dante one bit ... until lunchtime.

Chelsea: *(entering)* You won't believe all the interesting things I've found out about Peru's government here do you want to read what I have so far?

Dante: I'm trying to eat lunch, Chelsea!

Chelsea: Oh I'm sorry that was so rude you go ahead and eat and I'll just sit down here and wait until you're finished.

Luke: *(mutters)* Great.

Dante: Aren't you going to eat any lunch, Chelsea?

Chelsea: I already had a turkey sandwich from home hey Annamarie that's what you should be eating you know because of your report.

Annamarie: But my report is on Greece.

Chelsea: Yeah but *Greece* isn't good for you get it *grease* so you'd better stick to something healthy like *Turkey* get it *turkey*?

Jed: We. Get. It.

Porter: *(kindly)* Yeah. Good one.

Dante: They have ice cream bars today, Chelsea. Don't you want one?

Chelsea: No I had a big sandwich and I'm not really—

Others: Don't say it!

Chelsea: What?

Dante: Never mind. Well … I'd better get going. *(exits)*

Others: *(exiting)* Me, too. Gotta go. Later! *Etc.*

Chelsea: Well that was strange they didn't even finish their lunches I guess they weren't very—

Narrator: *(loudly)* So since everybody else left the cafeteria, Chelsea decided to leave, too.

Chelsea: *(exiting)* I guess I might as well I mean why hang around when …

Scene Six

Narrator: Soon Dante was wishing he could move away like Julius.

Dante: *(entering)* Or get suspended. Or lost in a cave. Or kidnapped by aliens. Or—

Narrator: Every time he turned around, Chelsea was there.

Chelsea: (*entering*) Peru's coastline is almost 1,500 miles long no wonder they do a lot of fishing there oh and they farm too they export asparagus and coffee isn't that interesting?

Dante: Sure. (*after Chelsea exits*) We're supposed to work separately, but she doesn't get that.

Chelsea: (*entering*) Mining is important to Peru's economy they're like really big producers of silver and gold and copper cool huh?

Dante: Yeah. (*after Chelsea exits*) It's not a difficult concept. I do my part ... alone. She does—

Chelsea: (*entering*) They also mine guano in Peru that means bird droppings they collect the guano and make fertilizer out of it I mean really guano! (*exits*)

Dante: Aaargh! She! Is! So! Annoying!

Chelsea: (*entering*) Have you heard of the Pan-American Highway it's this really long—

Dante: Sheesh! You don't have to keep telling me this stuff. Just put it all in the project.

Chelsea: But I'm keeping you informed we are doing this project together so—

Dante: You don't have to do that! You don't have to talk at all! Just give me your stuff later.

Chelsea: Wait I see what's going on here I've been talking too much haven't I?

Dante: Well ... yes!

Chelsea: I am so sorry I have a bad habit of doing that but I want this partnership to work so I'm going to stop doing that right now.

Dante: Oh. OK. Thanks.

Chelsea: So tell me all about your part of the project have you found out anything interesting about Peru's history like is there anybody famous from Peru go ahead I'm all ears.

Dante: You don't ... I meant ... Don't you ... I have to go! (*exits*)

Chelsea: Wow I'm *Havana* hard time finishing a conversation with anybody ha that's a good one wait Havana is a city not a country so it doesn't really fit with my other jokes does it?

Narrator: *(frustrated)* Does it really matter? Nobody cares if your jokes are—

Chelsea: *(exiting)* I wonder if Dante has found out about the cities in Peru I'd better ask him about that where did he …

Narrator: Brother.

Scene Seven

Narrator: *(as Dante and Porter enter)* Porter's plan had sounded so perfect, but obviously it wasn't going to work at all.

Dante: Your stupid plan isn't working!

Porter: What stupid plan?

Dante: How many stupid plans do you have? I'm talking about your idea for how I could work with Chelsea long-distance.

Porter: Oh. That stupid plan. She sure is hanging around a lot.

Dante: I know! I've tried to get her to understand the idea of working separately, but it's hopeless. So what do I do now?

Porter: I don't know. One stupid plan per week is my limit.

Dante: Thanks. I'll have to think of something myself. *(pauses)* This might take a while …

Narrator: And while Dante was trying to come up with a new plan for handling Chelsea, the situation got even worse. Chelsea kept buzzing around Dante like a fly around garbage.

Dante: He-e-ey …

Narrator: *(as Jed, Annamarie, and Luke enter)* Well … you know what I mean. And after a few more days of being Chelsea's partner, Dante was ready to explode.

Annamarie: Finally—lunch time! I'm starving.

Luke: Does anybody want to trade … Oh, no!

Chelsea: *(entering)* Hi Dante can I sit by you thanks hey *Jamaica* map of Peru yet get it *did you make a* map it's a joke so anyway let's hear about your map.

Jed: Ooh, yes, Dante. Tell us about your map.

Dante: Funny. *(to Chelsea)* Look, I don't want to talk about schoolwork at lunch.

Chelsea: Oh sure I understand we can talk about whatever you want like how are things with your family who's in your family anyway oh do you have any pets?

Dante: I don't want to talk, OK?

Chelsea: I'm sorry I was just being friendly I didn't know your family was a touchy subject I wouldn't have brought them up—

Dante: I don't want to talk to *you*! How can I make that any plainer? Oh, I know! Let me put it this way: you're nothing *Budapest!*

Others (except Porter): Ha! Good one! You said it! *Etc.*

Chelsea: I don't get it oh I see it's a joke *Budapest* it's like *but a pest* but you know Dante Budapest is a city not a country and … wait … did you mean … oh.

Dante: So … you do your part. I'll do my part. We'll put it together in the end. OK?

Chelsea: Um … sure. *(exits)*

Luke: Thanks, Dante! She drives me crazy.

Annamarie: She drives everybody crazy.

Porter: Yeah, but … I mean … never mind.

Scene Eight

Narrator: *(as Jed, Annamarie, and Luke exit)* Dante was feeling pretty darn good about getting rid of Chelsea … until he noticed the look on Porter's face.

Dante: What's the matter?

Porter: You really hurt Chelsea's feelings.

Dante: I had to do it. It's bad enough that she keeps bugging me about the project. Now she thinks she's my friend? I had to put a stop to that right away.

Porter: So she's kind of annoying—

Dante: Kind of?

Porter: But she's not a bad person—

Dante: Except for being incredibly annoying.

Porter: She tries to be positive and—

Dante: Annoying.

Porter: Listen! It's hard to be nice to some people, but you have to look past the annoying stuff.

Dante: I tried! Chelsea is just too much! I feel bad about hurting her feelings, but it happened that way because she's so extra-specially obnoxious. It's not like I ever acted like that before.

Porter: Are you kidding? You never let Julius play ball with us.

Dante: But he was a terrible player! And his nose was always runny. Ew!

Porter: He had allergies, OK? The thing is: you weren't very nice to him. And you called Ellen names all the time.

Dante: So? She was always causing trouble!

Porter: Yeah, she was a pain, but that didn't make it right for you to tease her. And what about—

Dante: Look, I try to be nice to everybody, OK? But some people are just too obnoxious to stand! I can't be friends with all the annoying, sorry losers of the world.

Porter: No. But would it kill you to be kind to them? *(exits)*

Dante: I'm kind! Considering how annoying some people are, I'm very kind. Kind of.

Scene Nine

Narrator: Once his problem with Chelsea was solved, Dante got busy on his project.

Dante: I hate to say it, but Chelsea was right about Peru being a cool country. I've found out all kinds of interesting stuff about Peru's geography, and now I'm going research its history.

Narrator: That's when Dante read about Saint Martin de Porres.

Dante: Saint Martin sure had it tough. His Spanish father barely took any interest in him. And his mother was a freed slave who worked hard to feed Martin and his sister, but they still lived in terrible poverty. Wow ... even though they were poor, he gave food to other people.

Narrator: You mean ... to people he liked?

Dante: No, he'd help anybody in need. And later he worked for a man who taught him how to care for the sick. Martin helped a lot of people then. He didn't care what race they were or if they had money or anything.

Narrator: But what if someone was annoying? He didn't help people like that, did he?

Dante: I'm sure he did! And when he became a religious brother, he took care of the sick and he helped the poor and he started an orphanage and a children's hospital and he did all kinds of good work—for all kinds of people.

Narrator: Even obnoxious people? Even the sorry losers of the world?

Dante: Sure! Saint Martin looked for God in everyone and treated all of them … um … oh … man. When somebody turns me off, I don't even try to look any further. I just see the unpleasant side and stop there. And then I act like I don't have to be nice. But that's just not right. *(sighs)* Porter tried to get me to see the truth, but I wouldn't listen. Man. I am such a … such a …

Narrator: Sorry loser?

Dante: Yeah. At least I'm not annoying, too.

Narrator: Uh-huh.

Dante: Right. I guess Porter's pretty annoyed with me. And Chelsea … Well, she's way more than annoyed. I shouldn't have hurt her like that. I'm nothing like Saint Martin de Porres.

Narrator: But you could be *more* like him.

Dante: Yeah. I could really do a better job of looking for something good in everybody. I'm going to try to change how I'm treating people. Maybe I should start out with some apologies!

Scene Ten

Narrator: *(as Porter enters)* Apologizing to Porter wasn't too bad.

Dante: … And I'm really sorry, OK? I should have listened to you.

Porter: Yes, you should have. I hope you've learned a lesson.

Dante: Oh, absolutely!

Porter: Never, never listen to any of my stupid ideas.

Dante: *(laughing)* Got it!

Narrator: *(as Porter exits and Chelsea enters)* But apologizing to Chelsea was hard.

Chelsea: Here's my stuff on the government and economy. I'll have the flag tomorrow.

Dante: Thanks. Listen, Chelsea … I'm not into … um … talking like you are, and I got annoyed. But I shouldn't have treated you the way I did. *(softly)* I'm … I'm sorry.

Chelsea: Yeah. Well. I know I bug people. I just get all excited and then I start talking and I can't seem to stop and pretty soon … I mean … See? Well, anyway … it's OK.

Dante: Thanks. So … want to get together tomorrow and finish up the project?

Chelsea: Do you really want to do that?

Dante: Sure. I mean … um … *India* I do! That's no good. Oh. There's *Norway* I want to finish the project without you. Bad one. I *Canada* wait—

Chelsea: *(laughing)* OK, OK! If I say I'll do it, will you stop? Please?

Dante: We-e-ell … if *Yemen* it.

Chelsea: *(exiting)* Aaargh! See you tomorrow!

Dante: *(following)* Wait! I have a good one for Madagascar!

Narrator: Oh, he does not! Does he? Hmmm … Hey, wait! *(exits)*

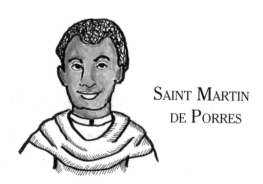

SAINT MARTIN
DE PORRES

Total Eclipse

SUMMARY

After a makeover, Harper develops a huge ego. Her friends get tired of living in the shadow of her big head! If only Harper could learn to be humble like Saint Juan Diego.

COSTUMES/SETS/PROPS

All can wear contemporary clothing, but costumes could be used for the TV Host, actors in the program, and Devonna Diva. Harper's criticisms of others needn't be based on reality.

A few chairs are needed for the TV studio, auditorium, and Olivia's house.

If props are desired, the following can be used: boxes in Christmas wrapping, an oddly colored scarf and sweater, a hand-made hat and gloves, and roses and a cloak for the program.

PRESENTATION

In the first scene, the TV program plays out on one side of the stage as Harper's friends watch from the other. The same setup can be used for the program in Scene Eight.

In her "before" mode, Harper lets her face sag, hangs her head, and slouches. In her "after" mode, she tosses her hair, poses, and preens. In the end, she looks happy and normal.

CAST

Narrator

Harper

Olivia, Mario, Callie, and Trent—Harper's friends

TV Host

Devonna Diva

Three Extra Kids

Virgin Mary

Saint Juan Diego

Bishop

ABOUT SAINT JUAN DIEGO

Juan Diego, a native of present-day Mexico, was born in 1474. He lived a hard life as a farm worker, but he had great faith, even walking fifteen miles to church. The Virgin Mary appeared to this humble, pious man several times, sending him to ask the bishop to build a church. Juan Diego's efforts to convince the bishop failed, so Mary provided a sign—roses growing in winter. Juan Diego gathered the flowers in his cloak and took them to the bishop. Miraculously, an image of the Virgin appeared on the cloak. The church was built, and Juan Diego served as its caretaker until his death in 1548. Juan Diego's feast day is December 9. He is the patron of those devoted to Mary.

Total Eclipse

Scene One

Narrator: When Harper got the big news, she was stunned.

Harper: I won a contest? Wow! And I'm getting a makeover? On TV? Wow! This could change my whole life! *(exits)*

Narrator: *(as Host, Devonna, and friends enter)* And it did! See, it happened like this ...

Olivia: I'm turning on the TV, everybody!

Mario: I can't believe Harper's going to be on television.

Callie: This is cool!

Trent: Quiet! The show's on.

Host: Welcome our special guest, fashion guru Devonna Diva! *(encourages audience to applaud)*

Devonna: Thank you! It's a pleasure to be here to share my genius with all the little people.

Olivia: Come on, come on! We want to see Harper!

Host: Now let's take a look at our first makeover. Here's Harper before ...

Harper: *(enters and poses in "before" mode)*

Mario: Whoa! She doesn't usually look like that!

Callie: *(as Harper exits)* They must have used bad lighting for the before pictures.

Host: And here's Harper now!

Harper: *(entering in "after" mode)*

Host: Stunning! *(encourages applause)*

Friends: Wow! She looks great! Fantastic! *Etc.*

Host: How do you feel?

Harper: I feel beautiful!

Host: Well, you look beautiful, too. Devonna, you are amazing!

Devonna: I know. I am also warm-hearted and caring to the little people. That is why I took the time to teach Hannah here how to maintain her look. Now she can be beautiful forever!

Host: That's wonderful. Thank you, Hannah.

Trent: Sheesh! Can't they even get her name right?

Olivia: *(as Harper exits)* I don't think she cared.

Mario: Yeah. She's on cloud nine.

Trent: She really seemed different, didn't she?

Callie: Oh, she's still the same old Harper.

Narrator: But she wasn't. Not at all.

Scene Two

Narrator: *(as Host and Devonna exit and Harper enters)* At first, Harper's friends didn't realize the makeover had changed more than just her looks.

Trent: Hey, here's Harper!

Harper: Hello, everyone.

Olivia: You look great.

Others: Yeah! Wonderful! *Etc.*

Harper: Thanks. Devonna really knows her stuff. I learned a lot from her.

Trent: It's too bad she couldn't keep your name straight.

Harper: Who cares? The woman is a genius! I mean … look at me.

Callie: You do look beautiful.

Mario: Wait. Didn't your hair used to be *(darker or lighter)?*

Harper: Devonna *(darkened or lightened)* it a bit. She says the color brings out my true beauty.

Trent: Your real hair looked just fine.

Harper: Who wants to look fine? I wanted to be beautiful—and now I am! *(pauses)* Right?

Others: Yeah! Sure! *Etc.*

Harper: Thanks. I don't mean to brag. I just feel so fantastic!

Olivia: Well, we're happy for you.

Callie: So tell us all about the makeover.

Harper: Besides my hair, *(tosses head)* Devonna also fixed my eyebrows.

Mario: What was wrong with them?

Harper: They weren't proportioned correctly. But Devonna plucked a little here and there, and now they're perfect! Devonna says eyebrows make the face.

Olivia: Make the face what?

Callie: They make the face beautiful.

Harper: Right. Good eyebrows are the secret. Along with the right makeup, of course. Devonna showed me how to apply makeup correctly. See?

Trent: We see it all right.

Harper: She also taught me how to dress.

Mario: *(snorts)* I learned that when I was two years old.

Callie: Mario! She means how to dress to look her best.

Harper: Right. And Devonna taught me how to stand and how to walk and … oh, just everything about looking beautiful.

Trent: Well … um … you sure look different.

Callie: Yeah, but she's the same old Harper we know and love.

Harper: Only better!

Scene Three

Narrator: *(as all except Harper exit)* Devonna Diva was right when she said Hannah would be able to maintain her look. Well … except that Harper's name isn't Hannah. But other than that, she was right. Harper looked great every day after her makeover.

Harper: Aaah! Another beautiful day! Oh. And it looks nice outside, too.

Narrator: *(as Devonna enters)* But Harper learned more than just beauty tips.

Devonna: *(slowly in a dreamlike manner)* Remember the little people ... Remember the little people ... Remember the ... *(fading as she exits)*

Harper: Hmmm ... What was that thing Devonna said about the little people?

Devonna: *(loudly and impatiently from offstage)* Remember the little people!

Harper: Oh, yeah. Now that I'm the new me, I should help the little people. Hey, there's Olivia! I'll help her.

Olivia: *(entering)* Hi! How do you like my eyebrows? I plucked them since you said eyebrows make the face.

Harper: Yes, well, unfortunately your eyebrows are making your face look lopsided.

Olivia: They are?

Harper: Don't get me wrong! I think it's great that you tried to fix your problem ...

Olivia: My problem?

Harper: But you should have shaped your brows like mine. See how they arch over ... Oh, never mind. They're ruined for now. When they grow out, I'll help you with them.

Olivia: Gee. Thanks. *(exits)*

Harper: That was really satisfying. I can see why Devonna loves her work.

Scene Four

Narrator: Things worked out so well with Olivia that Harper decided to help somebody else.

Harper: There's Mario. He really needs the benefit of my expertise.

Mario: *(entering)* Hello, Harper.

Harper: Hey, remember when you said that you learned how to dress when you were two?

Mario: Yeah. What about it?

Harper: Well, that wasn't true. You don't know how to dress. I mean ... those pants aren't the right style ... and that shirt only accents your bad points. And really ... what clown did you steal those shoes from?

Mario: These are my favorite shoes!

Harper: I know. And that is so, so sad. But we'll go shopping, OK? And I'll help you choose a whole new wardrobe. Just tell me when you want to go.

Mario: Right. I'll let you know. *(exits)*

Harper: Wow, isn't it lucky for Mario I won that makeover? If I hadn't learned all that stuff, I wouldn't know how to redo his look. He could dress like that for the rest of his life!

Scene Five

Narrator: *(as Trent enters)* Harper also corrected Trent's posture ...

Harper: Slouching is terribly unattractive. Stand up straight like I do.

Trent: I *am* standing up straight.

Harper: I know you *try*, Trent, but you're really not making it. Look at me. See how I hold my shoulders back? See how my good posture helps me walk smoothly?

Trent: I can walk smoothly. *(exits)*

Harper: That wasn't smooth at all.

Narrator: *(as Callie enters)* And Harper helped Callie, too.

Harper: Your makeup looks completely unnatural.

Callie: I'm not wearing any makeup.

Harper: Well, there's your problem! You need to wear makeup so you'll look natural.

Callie: But makeup is *un*natural!

Harper: Yes, isn't that great? You don't have to look like yourself at all.

Callie: Are you saying ... That's just ... Sheesh, Harper! I don't even know who you are anymore.

Harper: Well, thank you, Callie!

Callie: Brother. *(exits)*

Harper: There's nothing like helping the little people to make you feel big.

Narrator: *(muttering)* Yeah ... in the head!

Scene Six

Narrator: *(as Harper exits and friends enter)* Harper's friends were really getting tired of her superior attitude.

Olivia: She acts like she's some kind of expert, just because she had a makeover.

Mario: And we're her pet project. All that advice is so condescending.

Trent: I can't believe how much she's changed.

Callie: It hasn't been long since the makeover. Maybe she'll get over herself after a while.

Mario: I doubt it!

Callie: We should be understanding. Being on TV is exciting. It could go to anybody's head. *(as Harper and extra kids enter)* I'll bet she'll soon be back to her old self.

Harper: *(pointing to extra kids)* OK, you! Get rid of the pioneer look. You! That shirt just screams bad taste. And you! I'm sorry, but you are beyond help.

Mario: *(as Harper and extra kids exit)* Oh, she's not going to change! I say we kick her out of the group right now. *(muttering)* That'll show her ... talking about my shoes ...

Callie: But it's almost Christmas! I mean ... this is the season of love and good will toward all! You don't want to dump her now, do you? During the season of love and good will toward all?

Mario: Oh, OK. We can give her some time to straighten out. But if her head gets any bigger, I'm done with her!

Others (except Callie): Yeah!

Scene Seven

Narrator: Everybody tried to be patient with Harper, but the situation got so bad at their annual holiday party ... well, they just couldn't take it anymore!

Trent: *(to Olivia)* Thanks for having the party at your house.

Olivia: You're welcome!

Mario: Can we open our presents?

Callie: Mario! Don't you think we should wait until everyone gets here?

Mario: Actually, I was kind of hoping to escape before Harper arrives.

Harper: *(entering)* Hello, everyone!

Trent: *(to Mario)* Too late!

Mario: *(to Trent)* Yeah, but I don't have to spend a lot of time with her. *(to Harper)* We're ready to open presents now. You go first, Harper.

Harper: All right. I'll open the green one.

Trent: That's from me. I picked it out myself.

Harper: Obviously! I never saw a scarf quite that color. It doesn't match.

Trent: It doesn't match what?

Harper: Anything I own. But, thank you, Trent. I know you tried.

Olivia: Open mine, Harper.

Harper: OK. Well. Interesting. I thought Trent's scarf didn't match anything, but I was wrong. It actually matches this sweater. Who would have thought there could be two things that I couldn't wear with any of my outfits?

Olivia: You could wear them together.

Harper: I *could.* What's in this box here? Oh. A hat and gloves.

Callie: I made them myself.

Harper: But didn't you know that homemade accessories are out this year?

Callie: No. No, I didn't. *(exits)*

Mario: *(to Harper)* You upset her! Why did you say that?

Harper: Because it's true.

Olivia: But you didn't have to tell her.

Harper: Of course I did! I have a special area of expertise, and I shouldn't keep that to myself. It's only right that I share my knowledge.

Trent: Uh-huh. So everybody can be like you.

Harper: Well … they can try.

Mario: OK, that's it! Harper, you used to be nice, but since that makeover you have a serious attitude problem!

Harper: What do you mean?

Olivia: He means you're conceited. You act like you're better than the rest of us.

Trent: Yeah, like you're some kind of fashion goon now, and we don't know anything.

Olivia: I think you mean "guru," not "goon."

Trent: Whatever.

Mario: Your head is so big, Harper, it's blocking out the sun, OK? It's like a total eclipse, OK? And we're sick of living in the shadow of your humongous ego! OK?

Harper: I can't believe you're saying this stuff after the way I've tried to help you.

Olivia: Come on! Your "help" is all about you.

Trent: Right! You just help poor little us to make yourself look big.

Mario: And we don't need that kind of help. In fact, we don't need you hanging around us at all.

Harper: Fine. In that case, I'll just take all the lovely presents I bought for you and I'll go. You can keep that junk you gave me. Good-bye ... forever! *(exits)*

Callie: *(entering)* Where's Harper?

Olivia: We got rid of her, Callie. She won't be bothering us anymore.

Callie: Oh.

Mario: *(pretending to be amazed)* Hey, look! We can see the sky!

Scene Eight

Narrator: *(as others exit)* Harper was shocked by the incident at the party.

Harper: Total eclipse! That's ridiculous! They just can't stand the fact that they're never going to be like me. Well, I tried to help them, but, hey, I can't work miracles. I don't need them anyway. I'll just get some new friends.

Narrator: *(as extra kids enter)* But that wasn't so easy.

Harper: *(pointing to one)* You licked the pioneer thing, but, honey, my grandma looks more—

Extra Kid One: Hey, I don't want your opinions!

Extra Kid Two: Nobody does!

Extra Kid Three: Yeah! You're not as hot as you think you are!

Harper: *(as others exit)* They think I'm acting superior, too. This is so unfair! Everybody is assuming I have a big ego just because I look better and know more than they do.

Narrator: The last week before Christmas vacation was pretty lonely for Harper. People didn't even sit by her at the special assembly on the last day.

Harper: Not that I care.

Narrator: But Harper really was upset about how everyone was treating her—so upset that she didn't pay attention to the program at first. *(as actors in play enter)* But when she realized the actress on the stage was playing the Virgin Mary, she focused in.

Virgin Mary: Little Juan! Little Juan!

Juan Diego: *(falling to knees)* My Lady!

Harper: Oh! It's the story of Our Lady of Guadalupe.

Virgin Mary: I am the Virgin Mary.

Juan Diego: I can't believe you are appearing to a poor, simple man like me.

Virgin Mary: Little Juan, you must go to the bishop and tell him to build a church here.

Juan Diego: But I am nobody. Don't you want to send someone important with your message?

Virgin Mary: I am sending you, Little Juan.

Juan Diego: Thank you, Mother. I will go right away and do as you wish.

Harper: That's so cool how Mary sends a little guy like Juan Diego for such a big job.

Narrator: As she watched the play, Harper forgot her problems for a while. She felt sorry for Juan Diego when the bishop didn't believe him.

Harper: That's too bad. I guess the bishop doesn't want to listen to somebody so unimportant.

Narrator: And Harper was impressed with the way Juan Diego kept a polite attitude as he tried and tried to convince the bishop.

Bishop: I can't just take your word, Juan Diego. Ask the lady for a sign.

Juan Diego: Yes, Your Excellency. And thank you for speaking to me.

Narrator: Even though Harper had heard the story before, she was moved when the actors recreated a miracle on stage.

Virgin Mary: Go to the top of the hill, Little Juan, and gather the flowers you find there.

Juan Diego: Yes, My Lady!

Harper: Wow! Roses in winter! He's putting them in his cloak and taking them to the bishop. And when he dumps the roses out …

Bishop: There's an image of the Virgin on your cloak! It's a miracle!

Juan Diego: I can't believe Our Lady has blessed me like this.

Narrator: The rest of the play went quickly. The church was built, and Juan Diego was given a hut nearby. He took care of the church, greeted visitors, and told them his story, always downplaying his role and expressing gratitude for being chosen by the Virgin Mary.

Harper: *(as actors exit)* Wow. He started out with a humble attitude, and he didn't change—even when something super important happened to him. I mean … he saw Mary! But that didn't make him think he was better than everybody else. Too bad I'm not like him. All I did was get a makeover, and I'm acting like I'm the queen of the world. That is so lame!

Scene Nine

Narrator: *(as Harper's friends enter)* Harper wasn't sure what to do, but she knew she had to make things right with her friends somehow. She hurried to catch up with them outside the auditorium.

Harper: Hey, you guys! Wait!

Olivia: What do you want?

Mario: Didn't you tell us good-bye forever?

Callie: Let her talk!

Trent: OK. So talk, Harper.

Harper: I … I just wanted to tell you I get it now. I let that whole makeover thing go to my head. I can't believe how conceited I was! And I'm sorry.

Olivia: You really hurt people's feelings, you know.

Mario: Yeah!

Harper: I'm so sorry. I wish I could change all the terrible things I did, but I can't do that. I *can* change my attitude starting right now. I'm really going to try to be more humble.

Trent: No more bragging on yourself?

Olivia: No more so-called advice?

Mario: No more comparisons to clowns?

Harper: I promise! And if I slip up, you guys just tell me, OK?

Callie: I think we should give her another chance.

Others: OK. Sure. *Etc.*

Harper: That is so nice of you! Thanks!

Narrator: So Harper's going through another makeover now. She's dropped her superior attitude, and she's trying to act more like Saint Juan Diego.

Callie: You know what, Harper? These days you're looking more beautiful than ever.

Harper: Thanks, Callie, but it's just the same old me.

Trent: No … you do look different.

Olivia: Yeah. I don't know why ….

Mario: I do! It's because we can see her a lot better now … you know … now that her big head isn't blocking out all the light!

Narrator: *(as all exit, laughing, and Devonna enters)* And who knows? Maybe one day … um ….

Devonna: *(grabbing Narrator or unsuspecting audience member and leading offstage)* You come with me! I'm going to make you beautiful! No, no, you can thank me later. You know, eyebrows make the face! Make the face what, you ask? Well, let me show you ….

Saint Juan Diego

ABOUT THE AUTHOR

After more than twenty years as a special education teacher, Diana R. Jenkins became a freelance writer. She has written more than four hundred stories, comic strips, and articles for children and teens, as well as two earlier books of readers theater plays. Her books *Stepping Stones: The Comic Collection* and *Saints of Note: The Comic Collection* will be released in 2009 by Pauline Books & Media. Diana lives in Montgomery, Ohio, with her husband, a medical physicist.

Looking for more saints?

The Encounter the Saints series offers intermediate readers down-to-earth portrayals of the saints. Each story vividly recreates for the reader the saint's place of origin, family life, and corresponding historical events.

Paperback
120 pp.
#71168
$7.95 ($9.95 Cdn)

Paperback
120 pp.
#71028
$7.95 ($9.95 Cdn)

Paperback
104 pp.
#70943
$7.95 ($9.95 Cdn)

Paperback
120 pp.
#70641
$7.95 ($9.95 Cdn)

Paperback
128 pp.
#70749
$7.95 ($9.95 Cdn)

Paperback
112 pp.
#70919
$7.95 ($9.95 Cdn)

Stepping Stones
The Comic Collection

Denver, Chantal, Suki, and Alberto are on a journey—and young Catholic readers can join them! With these fun and inspiring comics, they'll share the ups and downs, problems and joys, successes and failures of a great group of friends. The stepping stones of their lives are leading them on a path toward God. Invite your students to follow along … after all, they're on that journey too!
Includes discussion topics for kids and information for parents and teachers.

Paperback
128 pp.
71184
$9.95 ($12.50 Cdn)

Pauline
BOOKS & MEDIA

The Daughters of St. Paul operate book and media centers at the following addresses. Visit, call or write the one nearest you today, or find us on the World Wide Web, www.pauline.org

CALIFORNIA
3908 Sepulveda Blvd, Culver City, CA 90230   310-397-8676
2640 Broadway Street, Redwood City, CA 94063   650-369-4230
5945 Balboa Avenue, San Diego, CA 92111   858-565-9181

FLORIDA
145 S.W. 107th Avenue, Miami, FL 33174   305-559-6715

HAWAII
1143 Bishop Street, Honolulu, HI 96813   808-521-2731
Neighbor Islands call: 866-521-2731

ILLINOIS
172 North Michigan Avenue, Chicago, IL 60601   312-346-4228

LOUISIANA
4403 Veterans Memorial Blvd, Metairie, LA 70006   504-887-7631

MASSACHUSETTS
885 Providence Hwy, Dedham, MA 02026   781-326-5385

MISSOURI
9804 Watson Road, St. Louis, MO 63126   314-965-3512

NEW JERSEY
561 U.S. Route 1, Wick Plaza, Edison, NJ 08817   732-572-1200

NEW YORK
Relocating. Please call: 212-754-1110

PENNSYLVANIA
9171-A Roosevelt Blvd, Philadelphia, PA 19114   215-676-9494

SOUTH CAROLINA
243 King Street, Charleston, SC 29401   843-577-0175

VIRGINIA
1025 King Street, Alexandria, VA 22314   703-549-3806

CANADA
3022 Dufferin Street, Toronto, ON M6B 3T5   416-781-9131